PICTURE P
VALUES

formerly IPM Catalogue of Picture Postcards and Year Book

Compiled by Phil & Dave Smith

Published by:

IPM
Promotions
130 Brent Street
Hendon London,
NW4 2DR

Tel: 020 8203 1500
enqs@ppv.uk.com
www.ppv.uk.com

Repro and Production by:

DX IMAGING
Unit 20,
25 Greenhill Crescent,
Watford, Herts.
WD18 8EA

Tel: 01923 227644
dximaging@dximaging.co.uk
www.dx-imaging.co.uk

Visit our website at:
www.memoriespostcards.co.uk

WELCOME TO PPV 2011...

Postcards are bits of cards which you post, but you knew that.

They can be pretty and attractive, containing nice illustrations, which have been drawn or painted, in oils or watercolours, photographic or typographic.

Postcards contain information, on both sides, not just the message side. The illustrated side can be full of fascinating facts, telling you stuff, hinting at stuff.

Postcards are portable. Not quite as portable as stamps, but then stamps are titchy and tiny, flimsy and weedy and don't tell you very much. They don't contain as much, not compared with postcards.

Postcards last. I have cards from the 1890s where the colours are still strong, the images clear, the surface clean and bright, unlike newspapers, which fade, go yellow and brittle. Just like humans.

Postcards are easy to maintain - you can keep them in albums which don't take up a lot of space, unlike furniture, and they never need to be dusted like your best china.

A Woolwich Arsenal defeat from the *Edge of Football*

Postcards are cheap, with many in full to the brim boxes at fairs starting at just 10p each. Even the most desirable, the most lusted after, never cost more than £1,000 - unlike stamps which can run into hundreds of thousands.

Postcards are historic. Through postcards you can trace the social and political and economic history of the last 100 years or so. Which I have just done. Well, one sliver of history- the history of football. By chance the golden age of postcards coincided roughly with the first golden age of professional football, when they both became entertainment for the masses.

Hunter Davies is the author of "Postcards from the Edge of Football" Published by Mainstream £20

WHAT'S NEW THIS YEAR...

We hope you enjoy this year's edition of the award-winning PPV, after we picked up the Desmond Chamberlain cup at Picture Postcard Show 2010 for last year's catalogue.

As always, we hope it will help you value your collection and also assist dealers among you who are looking for a specific price for a card.

We simply can't list every card produced, but with over 400 illustrations and 6,000 or more listings, we have tried to include a greater cross section than ever before.

This year... we have a special feature on Family History (p.189), which looks at the way Postcards can be used to help and enhance the research undertaken. This feature is written by **Penny Law**, Editor of *Family History Monthly*. We also have an introduction to postcards, above, written by Collector and Writer, **Hunter Davies**.

And we've added more names and prices to the Artists section.

Plus, with the help of John Priestley we have expanded and improved our Autographs section (p. 210).

We have updated the Overseas section, and we have looked at the whole catalogue, replacing every illustration and have reviewed pricing throughout.

Special thanks this year to Hunter Davies, Tony Davies, Bill Kirkland, Penny Law, Tony McKendrick, John Priestley, Tom Stanley, for all their hard work and contributions.

Phil & Dave Smith

AN INTRODUCTION TO POSTCARD COLLECTING

Here is a brief introduction to Postcard Collecting, a fascinating and rewarding hobby. We look at the historical background, and view the present state of the art.

The Early Beginnings
The first plain postcards appeared in Austria in 1869. One year later Britain followed, and shortly afterwards in the mid-1870s, the first picture postcards began to appear. The Paris Exhibition of 1889 gave a tremendous boost to this still novel form of sending a message, and from then on picture postcards were produced in ever increasing numbers by almost every country in the world. Britain joined the game in earnest in 1894 when the first picture cards were permitted and in 1902 was the first country to divide the back, thus allowing the message and address on one side and a complete picture on the other, a move which saw an explosion in picture postcard production as other countries quickly followed. This period is dealt with in more detail in the Catalogue under 'Early Cards'.

The Golden Age
The period from 1902-1914 has been termed the 'Golden Age' of picture postcards, for it was in these years that the hobby reached a height of popularity that it has never exceeded. It was a time when nearly everybody sent postcards, because in a pre-telephone era they represented the cheapest and most reliable form of communication. And what cards they were ! Almost every conceivable subject could be found on picture postcards, as publishers competed with each other to produce the most attractive designs. As a result, postcard collecting became a national pastime where almost everybody young or old had their own albums into which went cards showing Father Christmas and Fire Engines, cards showing Pigs, Pretty Ladies and Political Figures, and cards of just about any other subject you care to name! And the hobby was not confined to Britain, for by now every country in the world was producing postcards, resulting in uncountable millions being issued world-wide throughout this period.

World War I
For reasons of quality and price, the majority of British postcards had been printed in Germany, and the guns of 1914 brought this quickly to an end. But although the Great War did see many Patriotic and Military cards issued, in the words of Brian Lund, Editor of Picture Postcard Monthly, It 'destroyed a national mood '.

Between the Wars
From 1918 a number of things combined to bring about a virtual end to the hobby. A nation trying to come to terms with the tragedies of the Somme and of Flanders, was in no mood for the fripperies of the picture postcard. In addition, the doubling of the inland postage rate for postcards, the wider acceptance of the phone as a means of communication, not to mention the difficulties which many firms found themselves in after the war - all these factors combined to bring about the end. Perhaps quite simply, nobody, neither the postcard houses, nor the collectors, wanted to 'start again'. Of course, postcards were still being produced, but in much smaller quantities. The seaside comic market was still there, and some firms were producing local views, while others reflected the current Art Deco craze with some fine issues, but effectively the 'Golden Age' had passed.

World War II
The Second World War saw a minor revival in postcard production, with a number of Military and Aviation series being produced, as well as other cards dealing with issues of the time, but the hobby lay relatively dormant until the late 1950s.

The Postcard Revival
Throughout the post war years, a small band of enthusiasts had kept things going, until in 1959 two collectors, James Butland and Edward Westwood established a regular magazine. 'The Postcard Collectors' Guide & News, full of articles about the hobby, and closing with a short

sales list. 1961 saw the foundation by Drene Brennan of the 'Postcard Club of Great Britain', and at this time in the early 1960s, several collectors' shops could be found stocking old postcards. The hobby gathered momentum until in 1968 the compiler of this catalogue established the monthly 'IPM' sales magazine. This was the first real attempt to establish classifications for postcards and to put the hobby on to a commercial basis, and this issue also carried the first auction of picture postcards. From then on things further progressed. Postcard Fairs were already being held under the aegis of the PCGB and these were complemented by the first big specialist events held by John Carter, and in the early 1970s by RF Postcards. The hobby received a massive boost with the Victoria & Albert Museum Centenary Exhibition of 1970, later to travel round the country, and supported by an ever increasing number of books, magazines and sales lists, culminated in 1975 with the appearance of the first IPM Catalogue. The following year, 1976, saw the formation of the Postcard Traders Association, the first sale held by "Specialised Postal Auctions', now our leading auction house, and the foundation of the annual British International Postcard Exhibition, while in 1977 came the first Postcard Fair at Bloomsbury Crest Hotel, now an institution among collectors. Our regular monthly journal 'Picture Postcard Monthly' first saw the light of day in 1978, and set the seal on what has become known as the postcard revival. For now we had the dealers, the collectors, the fairs and auctions, and the magazines, books and literature. Everything was there, ready to move postcard collecting into the national hobby it has now become, taking its place alongside Stamps and Coins as one of the top three collecting hobbies in the country.

The Present Day
The hobby today supports some 500 Dealers and many more smaller collector/dealers. The internet has changed postcard collecting, with thousands of Postcards available, all categorised and easy to find with the search engines available. There are an estimated 20,000 serious collectors, many of whom belong to one of nearly 70 Postcard Clubs. We have over 20 Auction Houses specialising in picture postcards, and a national network of Postcard Fairs. There is the PPV Postcard Catalogue, a national magazine, and a substantial number of books on the subject. We can now look briefly at the operation of the hobby today.

The Collectors
Why do people collect picture postcards? Why do people collect anything! For pleasure, interest, and perhaps profit, are some of the reasons which may be advanced. Yet in this hobby, the collecting of postcards is now divided into two worlds. That of Art & Subject Cards, and that of Topographical, or Local History. The former are perhaps the 'real' postcard collectors, while the latter group are essentially more interested in representations of their own locality as it used to be, than in picture postcards as an art form.

The Dealers
The Postcard Trade operates in much the same way as the Stamp or Coin Trade, in that we have a national network of dealers whose task it is to find and supply postcards to collectors. Many of them carry substantial stocks of up to 100,000 cards, all priced, and filed in boxes or albums under their respective Subject or Location headings, although others carry smaller stocks, perhaps specialising in several chosen themes or areas. Many dealers will conduct business through the post, sending approval selections of your choice, while many more can be found at Postcard Fairs throughout the country. A comprehensive list of dealers will be found in 'Picture Postcard Annual', while dates of current Fairs are listed in 'Picture Postcard Monthly'.

Auctions
There are now 20 Auction Houses holding regular specialised sales of picture postcards. All produce catalogues obtainable on subscription, and all will accept postal bids for the Lots on offer. While the more common cards tend to be lotted in some quantity, there is now an increasing trend for the better cards to be offered as individual items in single lots, a reflection of the current strong demand for these cards. A word of advice, when buying at auction do try to ensure that cards are in the best possible condition, particularly if buying through a postal bid. This is made easy by certain leading Auction firms, whose descriptions always include a very clear statement of condition, but is less visible in the catalogues of some firms, where at times you will find nothing at all regarding condition.

Fairs

See page 10 for a list of Fairs Advertised in this Catalogue

Led by the gigantic IPM Promotions Fair which has been held every month for 30 years at Bloomsbury, London WC1, there are now over 50 organisations holding regular Postcard Fairs throughout the country, dates of which may be checked with the Diary published in 'Picture Postcard Monthly'. The largest monthly fair is the 'Bloomsbury', which every month has up to 90 stands packed with picture postcards and related ephemera, Other large provincial events include the 2-day Fairs held at York, Shepton Mallet, Twickenham, Woking and with major one day events at Cheltenham, Birmingham, Nottingham, Tolworth, Wickham and Haywards Heath. The prestige event, and most important show of the year, is the annual Picture Postcard Show (formerly BIPEX), held in early September at the Royal Horticultural Hall, SW1, while every weekend many smaller events are held regularly up and down the country. Here you will find the Postcard Trade at work, and will be able to meet the Dealers in person. Ask them for what you want, and you will find them all very helpful, particularly in guiding the new collector.

What to Collect

This depends entirely upon the individual. Visit the Fairs and look around at the enormous selection of cards you will find there. Perhaps after a few visits you may find yourself attracted to one particular Artist or Subject, or possibly you may wish to specialise in old views of your town or village. Whatever you choose, remember to look for cards in the finest possible condition. This is not perhaps so important in the Topographical field where only a few copies of a particular card may remain, but it is important in Art & Subjects. Generally you will want to ensure that the higher the price asked, the better the condition of the card.

How to Collect

At the Fairs. and in Dealers' advertisements, you will find a good range of accessories offered. Many collectors store their cards in albums, while others prefer loose storage in cardboard boxes. You may also consider it advisable to protect your loose cards by keeping them in protective envelopes now available. Some collectors prefer the old-fashioned Edwardian paper albums. rather than the modern PVC types. It is entirely up to you.

Postcard Clubs

As your interest grows, you may wish to join one of the many Postcard Clubs, a list of which may be found in Picture Postcard Annual. Here you will meet other local collectors who share your interest in the subject and who will be able to broaden your horizons by showing you some of their own collecting themes.

Investment

This is not something to be attempted by the new collector, for while it is always pleasant to see your collection grow in value, as indeed it will do, to set out to buy postcards with the sole aim of making money is an exercise fraught with difficulties. Wait until you know a lot more about the hobby. Then it may be possible to put some spare cash into an area you feel is under-valued, but a study of past Catalogues and past prices will clearly reveal that while some cards have risen dramatically in price, others have remained on the same mark for years, while some cards have even fallen in value.

Selling your Cards

All collectors wish to sell at different times. Perhaps they are giving up, or maybe turning to another subject. Whatever the reason, you have four basic methods of disposing of unwanted cards. You can take a table at one of the Postcard Fairs, and with your stock properly marked up and laid out, you can become a 'Dealer' yourself! If you know of other collectors in your field, you could offer your cards to them for sale by private treaty. Alternatively you can offer your stock to a dealer, but his response will depend very largely upon what sort of cards they are, their condition, and at the end of the day, whether he wants them! All cards must have a Catalogue value, but it does not necessarily follow that anyone wants to buy them! Most dealers will only willingly buy those cards in the collectable categories which they have some chance of re-selling at a profit. You can, of course, sell your cards on an internet auction site, which is readily available to everyone. Finally you can offer your cards for sale by Public Auction, but remember that here you take a chance on the final price. You may of course put a reserve on your cards, and if they fail to meet this figure they will be returned to you. You may be pleasantly surprised at the price you obtain at Auction, or in some cases you could be disappointed. Certainly you may do better with particularly good single items if offered for sale by this method, but you have to meet the Auctioneer's commission, which may be up to 20% of the price realised. If you have a valuable collection, you may wish to discuss various methods of sale with an established Auctioneer or Dealer.

Modern Cards

The past 10 years has seen a phenomenal growth in the production of Modern postcards, and this can be seen as almost a separate industry, with cards on every conceivable subject now being issued by many leading companies. After some initial hesitation by the traditional postcard collecting world, Modern cards are now making considerable inroads into the hobby. Perhaps the great advantage of Modern Cards lies in their price, where for a nominal 50p, or so, one may buy superbly designed and printed cards on almost any subject you care to name.

Conclusions

In this brief survey we have tried to show how the hobby originated, and how it operates today. It is still growing, and I sincerely hope that all of you, particularly if you are a new collector finding out about postcards for the first time, will gain through this, and through the pages of this Catalogue, something of the nostalgia we collectors all feel for those long hot summer days at the turn of the century. It was for many a golden age, a time of faded sepia, and croquet on the lawns. Of knickerbocker suits, Sunday School and Mr. Polly, when the event of the year was annual trip to the seaside, with its toffee apples, winkles and busy, sad-eyed donkeys. A time of endless summer, when small boys looked for tiddlers under the bridge, oblivious to the voices calling them home across the fields, peacefully unaware of the later call of destiny which they would face in 1916 in the green fields of France.

A time without television, video, or computer games, when young girls and boys spent their evenings carefully putting all their new cards into their postcard albums. It is these cards which are so highly prized today, and which form the subject of this Catalogue.

ACCESSORY SUPPLIERS

Vera Trinder Ltd. 38 Bedford Street, London WC2 9EU (See Page 6)	020-7836-2365
G. Barrington Smith* Cross Street, Oadby, Leicester LE2 4DD	0116-271-9181
Stanley Gibbons Publications 7 Parkside, Christchurch Road, Ringwood, Hampshire BH24 3SH	0800 611 622
Murray Cards International Ltd. 51 Watford Way, Hendon Central, London NW4 3JH	020-8202-5688
Rob Roy Cards Crosshall, Chelsfield Village, Orpington, Kent (See Page 7)	01689-828052
Taunton Stamp Shop. 66 Bridge Street, Taunton, Somerset	01823-283327

The firms listed above are trade wholesalers and between them carry an extensive range of Accessories including: Postcard Catalogues - Books - Albums - Leaves - Plastic Envelopes - Film Front Bags - Postcard Wallets etc.

Vera Trinder and G. Barrington Smith also specialise in Philatelic and Numismatic albums and accessories, while **Murray Cards International** and **Rob Roy Cards** carry large stocks of Cigarette Card albums and leaves.

Most of the firms above will deal with individual customers, but a telephone call will confirm this, and determine whether the firm have the item you require currently in stock.

In addition many postcard dealers carry smaller stocks of Books, Albums and Accessories.

*Trade only supplied.

GLOSSARY OF POSTCARD TERMS

Applique
A term used to describe a postcard which has some form of cloth, metal, or other embellishment attached to it.

Art Deco
Artistic style of the 1920's recognisable by its symmetrical designs and straight lines.

Art Nouveau
Artistic style of the turn of the century, characterised by flowing lines and flowery symbols, yet often depicting impressionist more than representational art.

Bas Relief
Postcards with a heavily raised surface giving a papier-mache appearance.

Catch-phrases
Many pre-1914 Comic postcards are captioned by phrases such as "When Father says turn", often alluding to other spheres of contemporary life.

Chromo-Litho
The finest of all colour-printing methods, the colour being applied in solids as opposed to modern screen printing. There are no 'dots' in chromo-lithographic printing. Cards produced by this method have a rich and deep colour, where often the original shiny surface remains. Usually found in 'Gruss Aus' and other early undivided back cards.

Composites
A number of cards which together form a large picture.

Court Cards
The official size for British picture postcards between 1894-1899, measuring 115mm x 89mm.

Divided Back
Postcards with the back divided into two sections, one for the message, the other for the address. Great Britain first divided the back in 1902.

Early
A term loosely used to describe any undivided back card.

Embossed
Postcards with a raised surface. Often found among Greetings and Heraldic types.

Fab Cards
Produced by W.N. Sharpe of Bradford. These cards contain a small printed silk square which could be removed and used for other purposes.

Full out
Usually found in the Heraldic classification, meaning a design which fills the whole of the card.

Giant Postcards
Novelty cards, some of which were as large as 305mm x 165mm.

Glitter
Postcards sprinkled with tinsel.

Gruss Aus
German for "Greetings From". A term used to describe these highly pictorial continental Greetings Cards.

Hold to Light
Referred to as "HTL". Postcards with small cut out windows, through which appear different colours when held to a strong light.

Intermediate Size
The link between Court Cards and Standard Size, these were cards of 130mm x 80mm.

Kaleidoscopes
Postcards where a rotating wheel reveals a myriad of colours when turned.

Midget Postcards
Novelty cards of size 90mm x 70mm.

Montage
A term usually employed to describe a picture formed by cutting up postage stamps.

Novelty
A postcard which deviates in any way from the norm. Cards which do something or have articles attached to them, or are printed in an unusual size or on strange materials.

Official
Postcard printed by a Government or other established body to advertise their services. The Railway companies printed many 'Official' cards.

Oilette
A trade name used by the publishers Raphael Tuck to describe postcards reproduced from original paintings.

Panel Cards
These are postcards printed on heavy board.

Poster Advert
A reproduction of an advertising poster, or a postcard done specifically in that style.

Pullouts
Postcards containing a strip view insert.

Real Photographic
Abbreviated to 'R/P'. Used to describe a card which has been produced by a photographic rather than a printing process.

Reward Cards
Given away to reward school-children for good work.

Standard Size
Introduced in GB in November 1899, this size of 140mm x 89mm corresponds to 5.5 x 3.5 in.

Topographical
A term used to describe postcards showing street scenes and general views, where the view is more prominent than any other feature, e.g. if a Post Office or Public House were to form the dominant feature of a card, then it would be classified and priced under that heading.

Transparencies
Postcards which change colour or reveal a hidden object when held to a strong light.

Undivided Back
Postcards with a plain back where the whole of this space would be used for the address. A term often used loosely to describe Early Cards, although undivided backs were in common use until 1907.

Vignette
Usually found on undivided back postcards, and consisting of a design which does not occupy the whole of the picture side. Vignettes may be anything from a small sketch in one corner of the card, to a design covering three-quarters of the card. The essential idea was that some space should be left for the message, as the reverse of the card could only be used for the address.

Write-Away
A term used to describe a postcard bearing the opening line of a sentence, which the sender would then continue. Usually found on early Comic postcards.

YORK INTERNATIONAL POSTCARD EXPO

110+
DEALERS
YORK RACECOURSE
APRIL 1 & 2
FRI 1st - 11am to 7pm
SAT 2nd - 10am to 5pm
DETAILS
01347 822722
01268 794886

2011

POSTCARD CALENDAR 2011

JANUARY
BLOOMSBURY	Sun Jan 23rd (see P.13)
BRISTOL	Sat JAN 29th (see P.17)

JULY
NOTTINGHAM	Tue July 5th (see P.19)
EXETER	Sat Jul 9th (see P.17)
BLOOMSBURY	Sun July 24th (see P.13)

FEBRUARY
NOTTINGHAM	Sun Feb 6th (see P.19)
EXETER	Sat Feb 12th (see P.17)
SHEPTON MALLETT	Fri 25 & Sat 26th (P.14)

AUGUST
BRISTOL	Sun Aug 7th (see P.17)
GODMANCHESTER	Aug 12th-13th (P.14)
BLOOMSBURY	Sun Aug 28th (see P.13)

MARCH
EXETER	Sat Mar 13th (see P.16)
BLOOMSBURY	Sun Mar 27th (see P.13)

SEPTEMBER
Picture P/C Show	Thurs-Sat 1st-3rd Sept (P11)
EXETER	Sat Sep 3rd (see P.17)
NOTTINGHAM	Mon Sep 5th (see P.19)
BLOOMSBURY	Sun Sept 25th (see P.13)

APRIL
BRISTOL	Sat Apr 9th (see P.17)
YORK	FRI 1ST SAT 2ND (P.9)
EXETER	Sat Apr 30th (see P.17)

OCTOBER
BRISTOL	Sat Oct 1st (see P.17)
EXETER	Sat Oct 1st (see P.17)
BLOOMSBURY	Sun Oct 23rd (see P.13)

MAY
NOTTINGHAM	Sat May 7th (see P.19)
BLOOMSBURY	Sun May 22nd (see P.13)

NOVEMBER
NOTTINGHAM	Sat Nov 5th (see P.19)
BRISTOL	Sat Nov 26th (see P.17)
BLOOMSBURY	Sun Nov 27th (see P.13)

JUNE
BRISTOL	Sun Jun 5th (see P.17)
BLOOMSBURY	Sun Jun 26th (see P.13)

Above is a summary of Postcard and Collectors fairs advertised in this Catalogue. Please contact the numbers given and please mention where you saw the advert.

BLOOMSBURY
POSTCARD & COLLECTORS FAIR
In the Galleon Suite at **The Royal National Hotel**
Bedford Way, London WC1

90 PACKED TABLES EVERY FAIR

POSTCARDS, EPHEMERA, AUTOGRAPHS, MOVIE JUMBLE, SPORTING MEMORABILIA, PRINTS, SCRAPS, PROGRAMMES, PHOTOGRAPHS, CIGARETTE CARDS, TRADE CARDS, CARTE DE VISITES, STEREOCARDS, POSTAL HISTORY, MAGAZINES, BOOKS, POSTERS, ACCESSORIES Etc;

TOP DEALERS AT EVERY FAIR

2010 FAIRS SUNDAYS
NOVEMBER 28TH
DECEMBER 19TH
2011 FAIRS SUNDAYS
JANUARY 23RD
MARCH 27TH
MAY 22ND
JUNE 26TH
JULY 24TH
AUGUST 28TH
SEPTEMBER 25TH
OCTOBER 23RD
NOVEMBER 27TH

NO CONGESTION CHARGE!

Admission £1.50
Open 10 a.m. to 4.30p.m.
(Incl. FREE postcard)
Early entry available at 8.00 a.m.

I P M PROMOTIONS 130 Brent St, Hendon, London NW4.
Tel , 020 8202 9080 020 8203 1500
Fax 020 8203 7031
e-mail dave@memoriespostcards.co.uk
www.memoriespostcards.co.uk

14

15

16

POST CARD

COLLECTION INSURANCE POLICY

Dear Collector

Just thought I would drop you a line about a Collection Insurance Policy offered by The Bateman Group.

The policy's key features include:
- Worldwide all risks cover
- Guaranteed values
- Depreciation paid if damaged
- Claims settlement option on sets
- No warranties or Average Clause
- Interest free monthly instalments

For more information speak to Chris or Dawn, their contact details are opposite.

Regards
A.N. Collector

P.S. Wish you were insured here!

The Bateman Group
QUALITY WITH INTEGRITY
Since 1967

53 Smith Street

Warwick

CV34 4HU

Tel: 01926 405880
Fax: 01926 410002

E-mail: enquiries@bateman-group.co.uk
Website: www.bateman-group.co.uk

John Bateman Insurance Consultants Limited is authorised and regulated by the Financial Services Authority (Registered No. 311378) for general insurance business.

2011 POSTCARD FAIRS

EXETER

Clyst Vale College Broadclyst
EX5 3AJ

Sat 12 February,
Sat 12 March,
Sat 30 April,
Sat 9 July,
Sat 3 September,
Sat 8 October,
Sat 19 November

10 till 4
(stallholders 8 am)
Postcards, Cigarette Cards, Ephemera, Stamps

BRISTOL

B.A.W.A. Leisure Centre
589 Southmead Road
BS34 7RG

Sat 29 January,
Sat 9 April,
SUN 5 June,
SUN 7 August,
Sat 26 November

Clyst Vale Community College, Broadclyst

Broadclyst — To Cullompton — CVCC

Pinhoe — Old A38 — Exeter — Old A30 — New A30 — To Honiton

B.A.W.A. Leisure Centre (589 Southmead Road)

J15 — J20 — J16 — M4 — A38 — Link Rd to M32 — M5 — Southmead Rd — Braemar Rd — A38 To Bristol

Anne Scott -
01395 270322
0771 573 6794

Check in www.postcard.co.uk
(Map)
or watch PPM for information

BRIAN LUND'S TOP 10 MODERNS FROM THE LAST YEAR

1 'Transport of Delight' have published many postcards of the Croydon tram network, with their

latest designs adopting a different size format that is squatter than normal postcard size. This is no. 2552, East Croydon station.

2 IPM Promotions postcards are given away to customers at their monthly Blooms- bury fair. This clever advertis- ing design for the event, using

the Routemaster bus, was published for the September 2010 event and is no. 298 in a series that began in 1978.

3 The final card – no. 500 – published by PH Topics, who have pro- duced so many interest- ing thematic cards since 1986. This finale was designed by York artist Brian Partridge, who has provided many of the PH images.

4 Railway scenes continue to provide excellent material for postcard pub- lishers. This one comes from Pete Shaw Photography,

no. 49 in a series on the Settle-Carlisle Railway, and shows Settle station.

5 One of the best current publish- ers of topographical cards is Photo- graphic Heritage of Raunds, run by Gordon Flanagan, who also takes the photos. This card (LE-0281) features

Oadby in Leices- tershire.

6 Contour Crea- tive Studio Ltd in New Zealand have produced many

original poster designs, put together by Rosie Louise and Terry Moyle on computer, like this one of Kaiwaka. Most of their postcards are aviation- related.

7 Reflections of a Bygone Age are carrying on a tradition begun in Edwardian days by publishing a series of 'London Life' postcards. This is no. 21, showing characters in summer 2010's 'Elephant Parade', which raised money for an elephant charity.

8 It is good to see a high-profile company like Barclays produc- ing postcards. This is one of 20 give-aways featuring electric moments from the Barclays Premiership.

9 The village of Keyworth in Not- tinghamshire posted a record number of 8,033 postcards on July 14th 2010. This is one of two cards pro- duced to commemorate the event.

10 Harold Jordan continues to be prolific in producing Ship- ping postcards. This is one of 20 recent releases and shows the SeaFrance ferry

19

LOUIS WAIN

Beagles
Coloured & Photographic   £35

Boots
Famous Picture Series of 12   £35

Davidson Bros.
Various Cards   £40

Dutton/N.Y.
Various Cards   £35

Ettlinger & Co.
Series 5226. Father Christmas Cats   £80
Series 5376. Father Christmas Cats   £80

Faulkner C.W.
Series 182 • 183 • 189 • 190 • 374
453 • 454 • 484 • 485 • 503 • 515
541 • 1596 • plus many others.   £35/£50

Gale & Polden
At least 1 design   £45

Hartmann
Series 3068. Fluffikins Family   £45
Series 3069. Manx Cats   £60

Mack W.E.
The Cat's Academy (Not all by Wain)   £30

Nister E.
Series 353 • 355 etc.   £35
Valentine series   £6
Philco series 2093   £35

Salmon series various cards   £35

Theo Stroefer
Usually unsigned designs   £25

Tuck R. & Sons
Series 130. Black/White und. back   £20

Theatre Series 3885 • 3895 B/W   £45

Write-Away Series
539 • 956 • 957 • 1003 • 1004   £35

Chromo-Litho Series
1260 • 1261 • 1262 • 1735 • 1748
1749 • 1782 • 5802 • 5892   £30

Chromo-Litho Nursery Rhymes/
Christmas/Pantomime
Series 297 • 298 • 8126 • 8127   £100

Diabolo Series 9563   £45

Dressing Dolls Fairy Tales
Oilette 3385   £100+

Oilette and similar Series
1412 • 3266 • 6075 • 6084 • 6401
6444 • 8515 • 8612 • 8613 • 8614
8615 • 8816 • 8817 • 8826 • 8850
8864 • 9396 • 9540 • 9541   £35

Others/Odd cards/
Part Sets inc. C132/133   £30

Valentine
Coloured Series/Un-numbered   £40
Charlie Chaplin cards   £100

Wrench
Pantomime/Black Cat Series   £50

Anon
Jackson's Hats & Boots/Poster Type   £75
WW1 Set including a cat `Kaiser'   £75

Many other cards exist, sometimes pirate copies, often with Wain's signature removed. There are also a number of unsigned cards by other artists done in the Wain style. All prices above are for single cards. A complete set may attract a premium over this figure. It must be noted that prices apply to cards in flawless condition, with no marks or damage of any kind.

Tuck series Diabolo 9563, £45

WHAT THE PRICES MEAN

With a few exceptions, all cards in this Catalogue have been given a single price, representing a broad average figure for the majority of cards in their respective classification. For example:

ART and SUBJECT CARDS

The stated price may be taken as a broad average figure for all Art and Subject cards. You will find C.E. Flower listed at £2. There are many common cards by this artist which are worth no more than £1, while his rare cards would certainly be worth £3. The great bulk of his output therefore would be expected to sell at the broad average figure of £2.

TOPOGRAPHICAL and SOCIAL HISTORY

With any relevant entry, e.g. Motor Bus .Tram . Street Market . Windmill etc. the stated price, or broad average figure, is for a card, *either RP or Printed, fully identified and showing a 'Close-up at a named location',* with real photographic cards being the most desirable. (Logically it will be appreciated that to qualify for listing at all, a Bus or Tram etc. has to be a *"Close-up"* in the first place and as such would represent the *majority of cards in that classification*). Generally speaking, anything less would be classified as a street scene at a lower price. If you think of a Bus or Tram in the middle distance, that is a street scene, while a Windmill in the middle-distance would similarly be priced at a lower figure.

With this in mind, it is then necessary to apply certain other criteria before formulating a final price, as with all Topographical and Social History cards, it is neither realistic nor practical to subdivide each entry into considerations of: Real Photographic . Printed . Close-up . Far Distance . Located . Unlocated . Identified . Unidentified . Common . Scarce . Publisher . Condition etc., not to mention whether the card is in a saleable area or even if it forms part of a remaindered stock! (You will begin to appreciate the problems in pricing these cards!). Put simply, the card has to be a Close-up to qualify for the price given. Consideration of all these other factors will then enable you to arrive at a final valuation.

A real photographic Motor Bus is catalogued at £35. A distant view of a Bus trundling along a country road may fetch £5, while a common, mass produced card of Buses in Trafalgar Square would only be worth 50p. On the other hand, a spectacular real photograph of a bus in a provincial town, taken by a local photographer, where the image fills the whole of the card, may fetch £50. Real Photographic cards are generally worth more than Printed cards, but a middle distance RP would be worth less than a superb Printed close-up. Admittedly, this is not easy for collectors new to the hobby, but as you gain more knowledge you will quickly see how it all works! Pricing is not an exact science, nor would we ever wish it to be!

It is further pointed out that in all relevant classifications, 'Accidents' would carry a price toward the higher end of the scale.

FURTHER INFORMATION

It must always be borne in mind that an exceptional card or complete set in any classification may fetch a price well in excess of Catalogue valuation. There are many reasons for this. In the dealer's stock any particularly rare or desirable item may be felt to be worth a premium, given the number of potential buyers, while at auction the same card, or complete set, would be offered to a totally different world-wide clientele, with a resulting number of high bids being received. It does not therefore follow that any auction realisation can be taken as representing current market value as perceived by the majority of dealers throughout the country.

In many Subject classifications, for example, Animals, Children, Greetings etc. one finds many cards printed by the early chromo-litho method. The superior quality of these cards would put them at the higher end of the price range.

It is not possible to be more specific given the huge numbers and types of postcards produced, neither is it realistic to have an entry for 'Chromo-Litho' under hundreds of Subject listings!

A single figure has been for all classifications where the majority of cards are of similar content, e.g. Bamforth Song Cards. One would expect to find such cards in any dealer's stock, priced at around the stated price.

The Price Range has been retained for classifications where one finds a wide divergence of content in available cards, e.g. 'Advert Cards/Poster Type'. Here only knowledge and experience can be your guide, though it is quite practical to take a middle average price for any particular card. This will enable you to form a realistic assessment of the value of your collection.

Unless otherwise stated, all cards in this catalogue are priced as being commercially published. Private and family photographs have no value other than what they may be worth to a particular collector. There are certain exceptions e.g. 'Contemporary Fashion, Weddings' and similar collectable cards.

Unless clearly stated in the text, all prices are for single cards.

In all cases, prices are for cards in fine condition, with no marks or bent corners etc. This is particularly so with Art and Subject cards, whereas in the Topographical and Social History fields, the image may be felt to outweigh considerations of condition.

The cards listed in this Catalogue are with very few exceptions pre-1939 and all standard size 5.5 x 3.5 in. This date may be extended to 1945 for the issues of World War 2, and as far as 1970 for GB Topographical Views, Civil Aviation, Cinema and one or two other subjects as indicated in the listings.

Certain issues in the larger 6 x 4 size did occur during this period, and are listed as appropriate, but with the odd exception, this Catalogue does not concern itself with anything later than 1970 in either size.

All prices in this Catalogue, many of them covering thousands of cards with one figure, must be taken as a broad average of that particular classification. Please do not say "PPV gives £3 for this". PPV does not give £3 for this. PPV suggests £3 as a mean average figure for the majority of cards of that type. Some cards may be worth £1, while others may be worth £5. Please bear this in mind when buying or selling.

N.B. It must be pointed out to non-collectors wishing to sell cards, that perhaps 75% of all postcards are virtually worthless! Postcards are like Stamps or Coins, in that huge quantities of common, or low-denomination material exists in today's market. I refer to Greetings cards - Landscapes - Seasides - Tourist Areas - Churches - Cathedrals - common Foreign views etc. All these cards are catalogued, and all must have a price, but it does not follow that anyone wants to buy them! Such cards may be picked up from auctions or trade sources in bulk at nominal cost. Effectively, what dealers want to buy are the better cards catalogued at £1.50 and upwards, which they can sell again. Please bear this in mind when offering cards for sale.

MODERN CARDS

As a brief guide it can be assumed that while certain subject themes may have a value of up to several pounds each, the vast majority of subject cards can be purchased new for 50p or less and secondhand or used for a few pence each.

As for topographical views, the same price structure applies, although it is pointed out to prospective vendors that views of foreign holiday areas are worth very little.

ARTISTS / COLLECTIONS

The years at the turn of the century saw the production of a number of selected postcard series, now justly celebrated as representing the high-water mark of postcard art and design. In this respect France was very much to the fore, and I give below a list of these series, together with details of other leading European collections. This is almost entirely the province of the European collector, for although these cards do come along from time to time in our Auctions, the interest in Britain is limited to a few people.

Market Report
A highly specialised area which has seen steady interest, prices tend to be determined at auction, generally outside the scope of the UK market.
Present price ranges are considered adequate.

AUSTRIA
WIENER WERKSTATTE 1908-1913
Recognised by the title design on the reverse, these cards were produced perhaps as a reaction to the swirling lines of Art Nouveau, being typified by a spare and severe style which gave way to Cubism and Art Deco. Artists include: Mela Koehler and Oskar Kokoschka.
Price Range: £60/£2500

FRANCE
COCORICO
Probably the most celebrated of all French series. There are 12 designs only. Artists include: De Feure and Steinlen.
Price Range: £150/£750

COLLECTION DES CENT. 1901
A series of 100 cards by leading Artists of the day. Cards have this title printed at the edge. Artists include: Alphonse Mucha, Caran d'Ache, Jules Cheret and A. Steinlen.
Price Range: £50/£500

COLLECTION JOB 1895-1914
There were three series together totalling 78 cards. Reprints of calendars and posters from the period above. Artists include: Angelo Asti, Jules Cheret and Alphonse Mucha.
Price Range: £50/£300

CONCOURS DE BYRHH 1906
A competition held to select advertisements for this aperitif. 113 designs were published as postcards. Artists include: Maurice Denis, Raphael Kirchner and G. Meunier.
Price Range: £50/£300

EDITIONS CINOS 1898
A series of 35 cards by famous artists of the day. Artists include: Alphonse Mucha, Jules Cheret, and Toulouse-Lautrec.
Price Range: £100/750

GERMANY
JUGEND 1899
Three series totalling 75 cards, in the Art Nouveau style. Artists include: Hans Christiansen.
Price Range: £50/£300

BAUHAUS 1923.
This series consisted of 20 designs, with reputedly only about 25 copies of each design printed. Artists include: Paul Klee and Kurt Schmidt.
Price Range: £250/£20,000

CHROMO-LITHO

Generally acknowledged as the finest of all colour printing methods. Briefly, the design was etched onto a limestone block and printed in solid colours, as opposed to modern screen printing, where the dots can be seen through a strong glass. Chromo-Litho printing was used extensively for post-cards from 1890-1910, particularly in the 'Gruss Aus' and 'Early Vignette' classifications. The reader is directed to the specialist books in this field which will list many of the hundreds of publishers engaged in this form of printing.The price of any Chromo-Litho card may be found by reference to its subject or artist, but there exist a great many unsigned Chromo-Litho cards of general landscape type.

Chromo-Litho printing was used in the early period, this fine example of Naval art c.1900, would sell for £15

TOPOGRAPHICAL ART

In recent years the collection of chromo-litho topographical art has become popular in its own right. Prominent names in this field include Manuel Wielandt, Michael Zeno Diemer, Raoul Frank, Paul Kley, K. Mutter and A. Prosnocimi. These and others are listed in the main Artist index.

Many cards in this genre however are unsigned, and a guide to the price of these is given below:

French Views	£3
German Views	£4
Italian Views	£3
Swiss Views	£3
Other countries	£3

ART REPRODUCTIONS

Friezes/Red Border types	£2
Miscellaneous reproductions	£1

Chromo-Litho/Heavy Board

Misch & Stock/Sborgi/Stengel	£2-£5

Gallery Reproduction Series

Photochrom Co.	.75

Art reproductions were produced to a very high standard, but are relatively cheap £3

ART TYPES

Colouring Cards/Pairs

Tuck R. & Sons	£2
Miscellaneous Types	£1

Oilfacism

Tuck R. & Sons	£1.50
Miscellaneous Oil Facsimiles	£1

Hand Painted

Professional Work	£5
Amateur Work	£2
Mass produced	£1

SCULPTURE

Art Sculpture on black card	£1
Gallery/Museum types	.75

Montage scenes

Mastroianni D.	£2

ART DECO

Art Deco remains an important postcard classification, reflecting as it does the work of many leading artists of the twentieth century. Art Deco began in the early years after 1900, as a reaction to the swirling and complex designs of Art Nouveau. The style was characterised by a more severe and economical line, and was later to be inspired by cubism. It reached its height in 1925 with the Paris Exposition des Arts Decoratifs et Modernes, but died out in the 1930s. At its peak, the Art Deco style reached into many other branches of the arts, and its influence was particularly notable in the design of contemporary architecture, furniture and fashion. The 'Odeon' cinemas of the period are a typical example. Artist signed postcards are difficult to price accurately while unsigned work can only sell for what the buyer is prepared to pay.

Much current business is conducted through the auction rooms where this subject always sells well, with the better artists much in demand.

Left: Art Deco design by Nerman Strom £18

Right; Brunelleschi £100

Bottom right: Manni Grosze £9

28

ART NOUVEAU

This is a highly specialised field which, like Art Deco, reaches into the Fine Art World, with the consequent high price structure of many of its Artists. Typified by a swirling, flowing style, Art Nouveau reached its apogee at the turn of the century in the work of Mucha, Kirchner and Basch, among others, but died out about ten years later. Like Art Deco, the postcards are difficult to price, for although the style is quite popular with British collectors, most business today is conducted through the auction houses selling single cards, often at widely differing figures. It is fair to say however, that considerable opportunities remain for the informed collector, whose specialised knowledge may be used to advantage at postcard fairs or retail outlets.

The work of top artists is keenly sought by an exclusive clientele, with much interest coming from the USA and the Continent. Both Art Nouveau and Art Deco, however, remain a rather heady mix for the average British collector.

3 unsigned examples of Art nouveau postcards. These tend to sell for less than signed designs. These would range from £30 down to £15 for the card below

RAPHAEL KIRCHNER

Kirchner was born in Vienna in 1875 and died in America at the height of his fame in 1917. His work dates from 1897 to 1916 and during this time he produced nearly 800 postcard designs, grouped together in over 120 sets and other issues, published by some 77 separate firms. Kirchner was one of the leading figures in the Art Nouveau movement, although some of his later work lay more in the field of straight Glamour. His cards have been catalogued by Antonio and Pia Dell'Aquila in,"Raphael Kirchner and his Postcards" published in 1996. This magisterial work illustrates every known card and gives a full listing of all known publishers. Readers who wish to look further into the life and work of this great artist can have no better guide. All one can do within the confines of a general catalogue such as this, is give a brief guide to those cards which by reason of publisher or other factors, are most often found on the British market, together with an indication of price. This in itself can only be a very broad assessment, as many of these series were reprinted by other publishers, often in different formats, with added greetings or other variations. It is further noted that certain rare cards not listed here, can be worth anything up to £500+ each. One problem remains with Kirchner in that some of his cards are unsigned. There is not much we can do about this other than refer the reader to Dell'Aquila where every card is identified. What follows is merely a general guide which I hope will be of some help to collectors.

All prices below are for single cards. A complete set may attract a premium over this figure. It must be noted that prices apply to cards in flawless condition, with no marks or damage of any kind. With highly rated cards such as these, condition is everything and those in less than perfect state would be worth considerably less.

'Raphael Kirchner and his Postcards' may be purchased from: Reflections of a Bygone Age, 15 Debdale Lane, Keyworth, Notts. NG12 5HT at the price of £29.95 including postage.

A Quatre Feuilles Set 6 Girls' heads in clover leaf	£65	
Enfants de la Mer Set 10 Girls at the Seaside	£65	
Fruits Douces Set 6 Girls with fruit between green borders	£65	
Geisha Set 10 Scenes of Japanese life	£45	
Greek Virgins Set 12 Girls in beige & gold design *See also Tuck Listing*	£65	
Les Cigarrettes du Monde Set 6 Girls smoking cigarettes	£65	
Maid of Athens Set 6+ Studies of young girls Coloured	£40	
Bw series *See also Tuck listing*	£25	
Mikado Set 6 Japanese Girls	£50	

Santoy Set 6 Scenes of Japanese Life	£60	
Demi Vierge Set 6 Girls on gold background between green borders	£65	
Femmes Soleil Set 6 Girls' faces on background of sunrays Same designs on pale blue without sunrays	£65	
Erika Set 6 Girls' heads on floral background	£65	
Marionettes Set 6 Girls with puppets	£65	
Bijoux Set 6 Girls in goblet/heart shaped panels	£65	
Les Peches Capitaux Set 7 Girl with inset pierrot head	£35	
Kirchner Girls Set 24 Bruton Galleries Delta Fine Art Co. EC2	£25	
Kirchner Girls Set 12 Bruton Galleries Alphalsa Publishing Co. EC2	£25	
Les Amours de Pierrot Set 10 Girl with inset pierrot head on titled card Reinthal & Newman/New York	£35	
Librairie de l'Estampe/Paris Glamour/WW1 period. 32 cards Numbered and titled on back	£35	

Cards published in Britain by Raphael Tuck & Sons.

Connoisseur 2555
Salome
Girls' large faces with scenic background
Coloured	Set 6	£60
Black & White	Set 6	£30

Connoisseur 2642
Les Ephemeres	Set 6	£100

Three girls in flowing dresses

Oilette Connoisseur 2709
Flashing Motorists   Set 6
£60

Continental 3002   Set 6
£85
Continental 3003   Set 6
£85
Girls' faces in circle with mauve background

Continental 3004   Set 10
£85
Continental 3005   Set 10
£85
Girls standing in Flowers

Continental 4002

Continental 4003
Maid of Athens
Coloured	Set 6
£40	
Black & White	Set 6
£25	

Continental 4008   Set 6
£85

Continental 4009   Set 6
£85
Girls in panels with pink borders

Continental 4016   Set 6
£85

Continental 4017   Set 6
£85
Girls in panels with olive borders

Continental 4024	Set 6	£65
Continental 4025	Set 6	£65

Greek Virgins
Diaphne 3501	Set 5	£200
Diaphne 8902	Set 5	£200

Vitraux d'Art
Girls in stained glass windows

The postcards of Raphael Kirchner can be divided into three main periods:

The Early Beginnings:	1897 - 1899
The Golden Age:	1900 - 1907
The Glamour Age:	1910 - 1917

Above; **Geisha,** Scenes of Japanese Life, *£45*

31

ADVERTISING

One of the most popular and widely collected postcard themes. Many different types of Advertising cards were produced during the early years of this century, both by the companies whose products they advertised, and by the independent publishers. They range from the very attractive 'Poster Types', designed in the form of an advertising poster, or sometimes

Cibils advert series £20

reproducing an established poster such as Fry's classic 'Five Boys' design, to the many plainer types known as 'Giveaways'. These were published by the company for promotional purposes, and were often given away with the product, although many more do show themes such as the gathering, processing, or manufacture of the product. Companies across the whole spectrum of industry produced Advertising cards of one sort or another, and we have cards from the Food and Drink industry, Animal Feed Manufacturers, Newspapers and Magazines, the Tobacco Industry, and many more. In addition, many of the

Railway and Shipping companies, as well as other more specialised issues are listed under those respective sections. We also include 'Reward Cards' under the main entry, as these were given away to school-children for good attendance.

Market Report

Strong prices for Tom Browne poster cards have been noted this year. Generally, subjects such as Golf, Tobacco, Pens and Shipping are in demand. Prices for better cards are generally set at auction but many lesser types can still be collected for a modest outlay.

Shell Motor spirit advert Original series £35

POSTER TYPE

Beecham's Pills
Tom Browne designs £30

Beer & Baccy
Victoria State 1896 £30

Berry's Boot Polish £20

Bird's Custard £20

British Army
Recruiting Poster £30

Bryant & May £35

Cadbury's £40

Camp Coffee
Harry Payne designs £60
Other designs £30

Campbell's Soups
G. Weidersheim designs £25

Capern's Bird Foods £15

Cerebos Salt £25

Champion Vinegar £12

Claymore Whiskey
Defenders of the Empire £10

Continental Tyres £25

C.W.S
Pelaw Metal Polish £18
Other Products £18

Epps Milk Chocolate £25

Fletcher's Sauce £25
GP Government Tea £15

Gossage's Soap £25

Heinz H.J. & Co. £18

H.P. Sauce £30

Horniman's Tea £25

Hudson's Soap £25

James Keiller £15

John Knight Soap £25

Mustad Horse Nails £25

Nestle's Milk £30

North British Rubber Co. £30

Ovaltine £15

Palmer Tyres £25

Peek Frean
Tom Browne designs £25

Raleigh Cycles £35

Deering Poster type £25

Schweppes £12

Skipper Sardines £10

Wood Milne Rubber Heels £15

Miscellaneous Products £10/£30

Suchard Chocolate/Cocoa
One of the earliest companies to employ the medium of the picture postcard for advertising purposes, Suchard were producing cards from c.1890 onwards.

Early Vignette/Gruss Aus type £20

Walker, Harrison & Garthwaite VC winners £12

SETS & SERIES

C.W.S. Packet Teas
Dickens sketches/Trade back	£8
Time Around the World/Trade back	£10

Epps Cocoa
Nature series	£8

Famous Posters in Miniature
H.M.& Co.	£30

GP Government Tea
Set 6/KEVII at Windsor
Price per set	£130

Lemco
Coronation series	£15
Types of Lemco Cattle	£10

Quaker Oats
Smiles/Set 10	£12

Shell Oil
Original series	£35
Reproductions	.50

Walker, Harrison & Garthwaite
Phoenix Poultry Foods	£10
Viscan Pet Foods	£12
VC Winners	£15

For other Advertising cards on Aviation, Motoring, Railway, Shipping and Theatrical, please see those headings.

CHROMO-LITHO
Standard-size cards, mainly of French origin, and printed Chromo-Litho, usually in early vignette style. They carry the brand name of a product on an often quite unrelated design.

Arlatte Chicory
Tuck R. & Sons/Flowers	£10

Belle Jardiniere
Art sketches	£20

Chocolat Lindt
Children/Art sketches	£20

Chocolat Lombart
Children/Art sketches	£20

Lipton
Language of Flowers	£18

Scott's Emulsion
French Departments/Set 92	£8

COURT SIZE
These are among the earliest examples of Advertising cards. Smaller than standard postcard size, and usually printed chromo-litho in vignette style.

Hutchinson Novels
Literary adverts	£25

Johnston's Corn Flour
Some Methods of Travelling/Set 24	£35

Nestle's Swiss Milk
Military vignettes	£40

St. Ivel Cheese £20

FRIENDLY SOCIETIES
Not exactly Poster Type, although some very attractive designs may be found on these cards.

Grand United Order of Oddfellows	£6
Hearts of Oak Benefit Society	£6
Independent Order of Rechabites	£6

Order of the Sons of Temperance
Heraldic Designs	£6
Bridges/Castles/Churches	£10

Twentieth Century Equitable Friendly Society £6

POSTER TYPE/SERIES

FRY J.S. & SONS

Prices

As with Tuck Celebrated Posters, a wide divergence exists in the current market value of these cards. Some are very common, others remarkably scarce.

Tom Browne designs	£20/£40
With Capt Scott at the South Pole	£60
Other designs	£20/£40

Caption	Artist
Showcard Replica Series	
What's good for the bee	
His heart's desire	
A perfect dream	
The tired traveller	
On the top	
A perfect food	
Sweeter than honey	

Vivian Mansell &Co.

Unapproachable
This is my brother Billy
A source of delight
Is the best
Keeps out the cold

Various Publishers

John Bull says support home industries	R.C. Carter
Cow being milked	R.C. Carter
The prize winner	Chas. Pears
If you feel cold	Chas. Pears
My eye! Ain't Fry's Chocolate nice	Chas. Pears
Far too good to share	Chas. Pears
The diver's lucky find	
Cocoa Sah!	Edgar Filby
Good old mater	
Fry's Milk Chocolate (White Cow)	
A perfect breakfast table	
Fry's Milk Chocolate (Pyjama boy)	
With Capt. Scott at the South Pole	
Keeps out the cold	
No better food after a good bath	Maud Fabian
The five senses	
Five girls want	
Always merry and bright	Ernest Noble
Great Scott! What a find.	John Hassall
Avec les compliments	
Disgraced but not defeated	Edgar Filby
I fully endorse	
I am ... etc.	
Yes, it's Fry's	

It's worth the risk	
Unrivalled ... etc.	
A double first	
The bloom of health	
No better food	
Design as above/C.W. Faulkner	
The little connoisseur	
Over the top and the best of luck	
Fry's for good	
So near and yet so far	Tom Browne
Highway robbery	Tom Browne
See their eyes as she buys	
Fry's	Tom Browne
One touch of nature	Tom Browne
Right up to date	Tom Browne
Fry's Cocoa (rich girl)	Tom Browne
Hello Daddy	
Whom God preserve	
Compliments of J.S. Fry & Sons Ltd.	
Fry's Coca (Boy with train)	
Fry's Chocolate for endurance	
Well, if you know of a better cocoa!	
Going by leaps and bounds	
Jolly good for the money	
Sustaining and invigorating	
Fry's, it's good	
The best is good enough for me	
Fry's Pure Cocoa/	
Design as above/J.S. Fry & Sons Ltd.	
Tuck CP 1500	Gordon Browne
Fry's Milk Chocolate/Tuck CP 1502	

TUCK R. & SONS
Celebrated Posters

Prices

There exists a considerable variance in price for these cards, even for the same card, if sold at auction or by a dealer. Basically the lower numbered series are the more common, and would range from about £15-£30 depending upon the artist, design, product, condition etc. But even here we find particular cards occurring more frequently than the others. Indeed some are positively commonplace!

The higher series from 1504 onwards are less often found, with the contrary position that certain cards seem almost non-existent! Here the price range would be from £30-£75, although prices as high as £150 for particular cards have been noted in the stocks of certain dealers!

For a more comprehensive study of this subject we recommend 'The Picture Postcards of Raphael Tuck & sons'. by J.H.D.Smith.

TOBACCO

A special classification for these cards reflects a shared interest with the cigarette card world.

Adkins Tobacco
Tom Browne posters £150+

Cavander's Army Mixture
Poster type £25

Dimitrino Cigarettes
Chromo-Litho £15

Gallaher's Park Drive Cigarettes
Poster type £12

Gitanes Cigarettes
Poster type/Art Deco £30

Godfrey Phillips
Set 30/Beauty Spots of the Homeland £8
Set 24/Coronation Series £8
Set 26/Famous Paintings £8
Set 24/Film Stars £60
Set 48/Film Stars £60
Set 30/Garden Studies £6
Set 12/Jubilee Series £6
Set 30/Our Dogs £90
Set 30/Our Glorious Empire £12
Set 30/Our Puppies £40

Grapevine Cigarettes
Southend Lifeboat 1906 £15

Gray's Cigarettes
Views £3

Job Cigarette Papers
Vercasson/Poster type:
Chromo-Litho £50
Early vignettes £25

Lea R. & J./Chairman Cigarettes
O.E. Pottery and Porcelain/Set 24 £6
With supplier's imprint £8

Mitchell's Prize Crop
Glasgow Exhibition 1901 £75

Murad Turkish Cigarettes £30

Nicholas Sarony
Film Stars £3

Ogden's
Poster type £90

Players
Poster type £75
Other types £30

Sandorides Lucana Cigarettes
Poster type £20

U.K. Tobacco Co./The Greys
Beautiful Britain £2

Wills W.D. & H.O.
Poster type: Capstan/Gold Flake/
Three Castles/Westward Ho! £100

Miscellaneous Companies
Poster type £15/£40
Views etc. £2+

GIVEAWAY/ INSERT CARDS

This section covers those cards given away or distributed by commercial firms, news-papers and magazines, etc., for promotional purposes. Subjects depicted are varied, and often have no relation to the product adver-

BENSDORP's CACAO AMSTERDAM

tised. Here again the total number of firms who produced these cards is incalculable. We list below the more common and collectable cards.

Amami Shampoo
Prichard & Constance £2

Answers £4

Bazaar, Exchange & Mart
Comic sketches £8

Beecham's Pills
GB views £1.50

Bees Ltd. £1

Bensdorp Cocoa
Pierrots £15
Dutch Scenes £6
London views £6
Isle of Marken £1.50

Books/Magazines/Newspapers
Military/Mail/Front Page £3
French Newspapers/Front Page £3
Other publications £3

Boon's Cocoa
European views .75

Bovril
Art Reproductions £1

Brett's Publications		**Colman's Starch**	
GB views	£1.50	Postmen of the Empire	£12
British Dominions Insurance		GB sketches	£3
Art studies/Set 24	£1.50	**Connoisseur**	
Bromo Cocoa		Art Reproductions	.50
Plantation sketches	£2	**Cook E./Lightning Series**	
Brooke Bond		Aviation studies	£8
Silhouettes of Manchester	£12	**Crawford's Cream Crackers**	
Butywave Shampoo		Russo-Japanese war map 1905	£8
Film Stars	£3	**CWS Soaps**	£5
Cadbury Bros.		**Daily Chronicle**	
Bournville village	£1.50	Fashion adverts	£5
Canadian Dept. of Emigration		**Daily Express**	£2
Canadian views	£1.50	**Daily Mirror**	
Canary and Cage Bird Life		Fair of Fashions Competition	£2
Cage Bird Studies/32 cards		Beauty Contest	£2
/pc back	£5	**Daily News/Wallet Guide**	
/trade back	£3	GB views	£1.50
Capern's Bird Foods		**Daily Sketch**	
Cage bird studies/pc back	£3	The Daily Sketch Girl	£3
/trade back	£1.50	**Dainty Novels**	
Captain Magazine		Greetings/Coloured	£2
Tom Browne sketches	£8	Other subjects	£1.50
Carter Paterson		**De Beukelaer's Cocoa**	
Removal trucks	£10	Topographical sketches	.75
Art sketches	£2	**Dewar's Whisky**	
Carter's Seeds	£1.50	Gems of Art series	£1.50
Chelsea Flower Show	£3	**Eagle Insurance Co.**	
Chick's Own	£5	Head Office building	£4
Chivers & Sons		**Elliman's Linament**	
Studies of English Fruits	£2	Tuck R. & Sons	£5
Aerial views of Histon	£2	**Family Reader**	
Christian Novels		Various subjects	£1.50
GB views	£1.50		

Knight's Soap Poster £25

My GOODNESS –
My GUINNESS

Guinness advertising £10

Feathered World
Poultry studies — £5

Field J.C./Toilet Soaps
Childhood sketches — £4

Field The
Military sketches — £4

Fine Arts Publishing Co.
Burlington Proofs — .75

F-M-N Complete Novels
Theatrical portraits — £1.50

Formosa Oolong Tea
Sketches on Rice Paper — £10
Japanese prints — £3

Fry J.S. & Sons
Non-poster types — £8
Views of Somerdale Works — £2

Garden City Association
Letchworth Garden City/
   Set 12/Frank Dean — £4
   Set 6/W.W. Ratcliffe — £4

Gentlewoman
Royal Artist Post Card Series — £4

Girl's Own Paper
Art sketches/4 designs — £10

Glaxo
Various subjects — £3

Goss W.H.
Oates S. & Co. — £8

Guinness A.
Cartoons/6x4 size/
Three sets of 6 cards (per card) — £10
3 sets of six cards produced on heavy card and larger size 6" x 4" with an envelope.
Set A. features Alice in Wonderland.
Alice Studies Natural History
Mushroom Growth
Why was the Hatter Mad
Bottle & Jug
My Mother Said....
Bottle Royal.
Set B. features Animal Posters.
Lion & Keeper
Pelican
Kangaroo & Keeper
Sea Lion & Keeper
Polar Bear
Toucan.
Set C. features "Guiness for Strength" Posters.
Girder
Pillar
Car
Tree Chopping
Wheelbarrow
Horse & Cart
Brewery scenes — £8
Brewery scenes/6x4 size — £4

Harland & Wolf
Valentine & Sons — £6

Hartley W.P.
Jam production scenes — £2

Haydock Coals
Art Reproduction/GB views — £1

Health and Strength
Physical Culture studies — £8
Hoffman's Starch — £1.50

Home Words
Various subjects — £1.50

Horner's Penny Stories
Various subjects — £3

Horniman's Tea
Invisible Picture — £8
GB views — £2

Hotels/Restaurants
GB/Artist sketches	£3
GB Photographic/Printed	£5
Foreign/Gruss Aus type	£4
Foreign/Later issues	£1

Ideas Weekly
The Imps	£8

Idle Moments
Various subjects	£1.50

Imperial Fine Art Corporation
Art Reproductions	.75

International Horse Show £8

Jacob W. & R.
Biscuit production scenes	£3

King Insurance Co.
GB Royalty sketches	£6

Lever Bros.
Port Sunlight village	£1.50

Liberty's £8

Liebig Fray-Bentos
Oxo Shackleton Expedition	£25
Meat processing scenes	£4

Lipton
Tea Estate sketches	£2

Liverpool, China & India Tea Co. Ltd.
Atlantic Liners	£15

Lord Mayor Treloar Home
Institution scenes	£1.50

Maggi
European views	.75

Manchester Dock & Harbour Board
Topographical sketches	£6

Mazawattee Tea & Chocolate
Louis Wain Cats/Postcard	£85
/Trade Back	£50

Mellin's Food
Costume & Flags/Set 12	£6
Various subjects	£6

Melox
Animal Foods	£6

Menier Chocolate
Paris sketches	£1

Miniature Novels
Various subjects	£1.50

Mirror Novels
Theatrical/Bookmark type	£3

Molassin Meal/Dog Cakes
Various subjects	£8

My Pocket Novel
Various subjects	£1.50

Above; Hotel Advert £4

My Queen & Romance
Various subjects	£1.50

Nestle's
Animals & Birds/Set 12	£6

New Zealand Govt. Department
Topographical sketches	£1.50

New Zealand Lamb
Dairy Farming scenes	.75

North British Rubber Co.
Golfing sketches	£45

Norwich Union
Motor Fire Engine	£12

Ocean Accident & Guarantee Corp.
Insurance Post Card Series	£4

Odol Dentifrice
Posters	£8
Actresses	£4

Oetzmann's Cottages
Exhibition cards	£1.50

Old Calabar
Animal Foods	£10

Oliver Typewriters
Writing through the Ages	£6

Overprints
Advertising copy overprinted on to otherwise standard commercial postcard.
Value as latter plus nominal premium.

Page & Shaw poster advert, £15

Nice design makes this poster £20

Oxo
Oxo Cattle Studies	£15
Oxo Football teams	£45

Peark's Butter/Tea
Various subjects	£2

Pears A. & F.
Various subjects	£2
Bubbles	£1

Peek Frean
Invisible Picture	£10
GB views	£2

Pickfords
Transport sketches	£8
Reproductions	.50

Pitman Health Food Co.
Ideal food series	£5

Poole Pottery
Phototype showing pottery techniques	£6

Postcard Connoisseur
Dore's London/1904 Facsimile	£50

Price's Candles
Military sketches	£8
Nursery Riddles	£8

Princess Novels
Various subjects	£1.50

Red Letter/Red Star Weekly
Greetings/Coloured £3**Remington Typewriters**	
Poster type	£20

Ridgway's
Tea Estate scenes	£3

Rowntree
Louis Wain Cats	£75
Rowntree's Postcard Series	£2

St. Bartholomew's Hospital
Reconstuction Appeal	£1

St.Ivel
GB views/Set 12	£1.50

St. Paul's Hospital/Set 12
£1,000 Competition	£1

Sainsbury's Margarine
Crelos/Early Days of Sport	£15
/Fairy Tales	£15

Selfridge Co. £3

Shippam's
Food production scenes	£5

Shops/Stores	
Artist sketches	£5
Photographic/Printed	£15

Shurey's Publications	
Twopenny Tube/Set 12	£6
Various subjects	£1.50

Singer Sewing Machines	
Sewing Machines Worldwide	£10
Aviation studies	£6
Battleships	£3

Sketchy Bits	
Various subjects	£1.50

Smart Novels	
Dance Band Leaders/Set 10	£6
Greetings/Coloured	£1.50
Various subjects	£1.50

Spillers	£12

Sportex Cloth	
Dog studies	£8

Spratt's Dog Foods	
Dog studies	£8

Sutton & Sons	
Flowers/Vegetables	£1.50

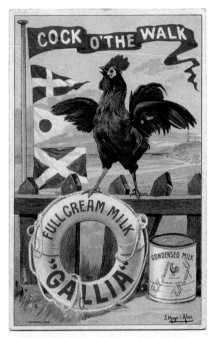

Gallia milk poster advertising £20

Swan Fountain Pens	
Comic sketches	£6

Symond's London Stores	
Comic sketches	£8

T.A.T.	
The 'Months' Series	£4
Other subjects	£1.50
Thomson D.C.	
Various subjects	£1.50
Thorley	
Cattle photographs	£6

Time Magazine	
Subscription cards	.75

Tiny Tots	
Greetings/Coloured	£8

Tit-Bits	
Poster type	£6

Tower Tea	
Proverb Series	£10

Trent Pottery	
Trent Bridge Publishing Co.	£6

Tussauds Madame	
Tableaux/Set 12/Tuck R. & Sons	£3

Trent Pottery advertising £6

Poster Advert, Baldwins Wool £20

Advertising poster type, Wood Milne Rubber political £20

Two Steeples Hosiery
Hunting sketches £3

Typhoo Tea
Various subjects/Oilette £3

Underwood Typewriters
Poster type £20

Van Houten's Cocoa
MGM Film Stars £5
Colouring Cards of Birds/
Set of 6 in Folder/Price per card £4
Dutch scenes £2
Art Sketches/Uncaptioned £1.50

Virol
Children of all Nations £6

Vitality
Physical Culture studies £6

Ward Lock
Naval photographs £3

Weekly Tale-Teller
Various subjects £1.50

Weekly Telegraph
Tom Browne sketches £8

Weldon's Bazaar
KE VII Coronation Souvenir £10

White Horse Whisky
Maggs Coaching studies £2

Wood-Milne Rubber Heel
Glamour studies/Sager £20
GB views £1.50

Wrench
Insurance cards £8

Yes or No
Various subjects £1.50

Chromo Litho printing Early advert, Quaker Tea £20

REWARD CARDS
Given away for good school work and atten-
dance etc.

COMPANIES
Cadbury Bros.
Birds/Set 25	£6
Birds and their Eggs/Set 12	£6
Butterflies/Set 32	£8
Map Cards	£8

Ficolax
Fruit sketches	£4

Milkmaid Condensed Milk
Royalty sketches	£8

Nectar Tea
Bird sketches	£6
Tea Estate sketches	£4

Reckitt
Naval History	£6

Scott's Emulsion	£5

EDUCATION AUTHORITIES
Barking Education Committee
Homeland Series/Court Size	£6

County Borough of West Ham
Court Size	£6

Erith Education Committee
Tuck R. & Sons/Castles etc.	£3

Hampshire County Council
GB views	£1.50

Huddersfield Education Committee
GB views	£3

Isle of Ely Education Committee
Nature Notes	£3

Leyton School Board/Pre-1902
Various sizes and series	£4

London County Council
Battleships/6 x 4 size/ S. Cribb	£5
Various Subjects	£1.50

Oxfordshire Education Committee
British Wild Flowers	£3

Reading EducationCommittee
Animals/Historical	£3

School Board for London
Various subjects/Pre-1895	£5
Various subjects/1895-1902	£3

Surrey Education Committee
GB views	£2

Walthamstow Education Committee
Paintings/Views	£3

Wanstead School Board
Flowers	£4

Gossage Soap, poster £30

Jacob & Co £15

43

ANIMALS

If postcard collecting was originally the province of the young girls of the Edwardian age, then it is to them, and their interest in this subject, that we owe the great legacy of Animal cards bequeathed us. Always an attractive collecting area, then as now. Animal cards were produced in considerable quantity, with almost every type of bird or beast depicted somewhere. Today's collectors tend to prefer Artist-drawn cards, rather than the photographic studies.

Market Report
Early continental chromo-litho designs showing frogs, pigs and insects for example are wanted. Artist drawn cats are always popular. Horses and dogs have gone a bit quiet.

ANTHROPORMORPHIC
(Animals in human dress)

Chromo-Litho	£10
Photographic/Printed	£3

BIRDS

NVP Sluis Birdfood	£1.50
Racing Pigeons	£5
Scilly Isles/C.J. King	£1
Art Studies	£2-£4
Photographic Studies	£1

Tuck R. & Sons

British Birds & their Eggs/	
Aquarette Series 9218/9399/9519	£6

BUTTERFLIES

Art Studies	£3
Photographic Studies	£1

Tuck R. & Sons

Butterflies	£6
British Butterflies and Moths	£6
Butterflies on the Wing	£6
Educational Series No. 8/Set 6	£8

CATTLE

Miscellaneous Studies	£1.50

CATS

Chromo-Litho	£12
Mainzer, Alfred/Post-war	£2
Art Studies	£3
Photographic Studies	£1.50
Inter Art	£6

DOGS

Military Dogs/WW1	£6
Spratt's Dog Foods	£8
Art Studies	£3+
Photographic Studies	£2

Dog Carts

Belgian/Netherlands	£4
French Milk Carts	£50+
French other Carts	£60+
Swiss	£5
Other European types	£6

Within these prices, named breeds would be worth more than un-named.

Frogs £5

Dogs Art studies £3

DONKEYS

Donkey Carts/RP	£6
Seaside	£2
Domestic	£2

FISH

Art Studies	£3
Photographic Studies	£1.50

HORSES

Horses and Carts	£6
Ponies and Traps	£4
Working Horses	£3
Art Studies	£4
Photographic Studies	£2

Coaching

Vanderbilt Coach	£12
Holiday types	£3
State/Ceremonial Coaches	£1.50
Old Coaching Inns of England/	
Set 16/J.C. Maggs	£1

PIGS

Early/Chromo-Litho	£12
Farmyard scenes	£3
Art Studies	£5
Photographic Studies	£3

POULTRY

Easter Chicks	£1.50
Art Studies	£4
Photographic Studies	£1.50

Tuck R. & Sons

Prize Poultry/Oilette	£6

TAXIDERMY

Booth Museum/Brighton	£2
Bramber Museum	£1.50
Stuffed Animals/Fish	£3

WILD ANIMALS

Frogs	£5
Rabbits	£3
Art studies	£3
Photographic Studies	£1

Tuck R. & Sons

Wild Animals/Oilette	£3

ZOO ANIMALS

Art Studies	£3
Photographic Studies	£2

Official Issues

London Zoo/Whipsnade	£2

Series

Zoological Society of London/	
H.A.J. Schultz & Co.	£5

Polar Bears, Art study £5

Our Dumb Friends League £15

SERIES

Tuck R. & Sons

Educational Series	£9

WELFARE SOCIETIES

Abattoir scenes/U.S.A.	£10
Anti-Bloodsports	£15+
Anti-Vivisection	£15
Cat Protection Organisations	£10
National Canine Defence League	£12
Our Dumb Friends League	£15
R.S.P.C.A./R.S.P.B.	£10
Vegetarian Society	£10
Veterinary Services	£15

ARTISTS

This is a select index of better known artists who designed for the picture postcard in both Subject and Topographical fields. It is not comprehensive, as many thousands of artists world-wide have contributed to the medium during the past century. The price stated may be taken as a guide to the most typical and representative work of the artist concerned, although in the Subject field, this price may be qualified by the theme depicted. With all artists so much depends upon the individual card, the design, the period, the publisher and of course the con-dition. I have done nothing more than indicate the general price area into which the artist falls,but certain rare cards by particular artists may dramatically exceed this figure. The great majority of artists listed below are either British, or have produced cards which are collected in this country. There are some excellent catalogues available which list the artists of France, Italy, Russia, USA etc. but I do not consider it practical to copy out several thousand names which would have little relevance to the British market. We have intoduced more new artists to the section and illustrations, which we hope will help.

Market Report
Attwell has started to sell well at auction again, A R Quinton has a very solid collecting base but many artists seem to have no collectors at all. There are plenty of opportuni-ties for collectors to find bargains at the moment.

M.A.	Comic	£1		Andrews, E	General	£1.50
S.A.	Comic	£1.50		Andrews, ET	Early	£10
T.A.	Comic	£1.50		Anichini, Ezio	Art Deco	£15
Abeille, Jack	Art Nouveau	£60		Anttila, Eva	Children	£6
	Glamour	£50		Aranda, Pilar	Art Deco	£8
Acker, Flori Von	General	£1		Ardizonne, E	General	£3
Ackroyd, W.M.	Animals	£3		Aris, Ernest	Comic	£3
Adams, C.J.	General	£1			General	£1.50
Adams, Frank	General	£3				
Adams, J.T.	General	£1.50				
Adams, M	General	£1				
Adams, Will	Comic	£1.50				
Addison, W.G.	General	£1.50				
Ainsley, Anne	Animals	£3				
Albertini	Glamour	£6				
Aldin, Cecil	Animals	£6				
Allan, A	General	£1				
Alanen, Joseph	Patriotic / Easter Witches					
	£10.00 - £15.00					
Allen, S.J.	General	£1				
Allen, W.	General	£1.50				
Alys, M	Children	£1.50				
Ambler, C	Animals	£3				
Anders, O	Animals	£6				
	Comic	£3				
Anderson, Alan	Railway	£3				
Anderson, Anne	Children	£6				
Anderson, V.C.	Children	£4				

Mabel Lucie-Attwell £6

46

Armitage, A.F.	General	£1.50
Asti, Angelo	Glamour	£6
Attwell, Mabel Lucie	Children/	
	Pre-1918	£12
	1918-1939	£6
	1940 on	£4
	Modern Repros	.50
Atche	Glamour	£30
Austen, Alex	General	£1
Austerlitz, E	Comic	£3
Austin E.H.S. Barnes	Animals	£12
Austin, Winifred	Animals	£4
Aveline,F	Glamour	£6
Aveling, S.	General	£1.50
Azzoni, N.	Children	£4
H.S.B.	Comic	£1.50
J.O.B.	Comic	£2
Baertson	Military	£4
Bady, Carlos	Glamour	£5
Bailey G.O.	Glamour	£4
Bairnsfather, Bruce	Comic	£4
	Theatre	£30
Baker, G.	Military	£4
Baker, H Granville	Military	£6
Bakst, Leon	Art Deco	£50
Balestrieri, L	Glamour	£8
	General	£4
Ball, Wilfred	General	£2
Bamber, George A	Comic	£2
Baness	General	£1
Bannister, A.F.D.	Aviation	£4
	Shipping	£4
Bantock	Art Deco	£8
Barbara, S	Art Nouveau	£25
Barber, Court	Glamour	£7
Barber, C.W.	Children	£3
	Glamour	£3
Barde	Flowers	£1.50
Barham, S	Children	£8
Barker, Cecily M	Children	£12
Barnes,A.E.	Animals	£20
Barnes, G.L.	Animals	£15
	Comic	£8
Barraud, A	General	£1.50
Barraud, N	Animals	£5

W. Barribal £12

Barrett, A	Military	£3
Barribal, W	Children	£12
	Glamour	£12
	Theatre	£25
Barthel, Paul	General	£1.50
Bartoli, Guiseppi	General	£5
Basch, Arpad	Art Nouveau	£110
Bask, W	General	£1
Bateman, H.M.	Comic	£8
Bates, Leo	Glamour	£5
Bates, Marjorie C.	Literary	£5
	General	£3
Baumgarten, Fritz	Children	£4
Bayer, R.W.	Flowers	£1.50
Beale, Sophia	General	£2
Beards, Harold	Comic	£1.50
Bebb, Rosa	Animals	£6
	General	£1.50
Becker, C.	Military	£8
	Sport	£8
Bee	Comic	£1
Beecroft, Herbert	General	£4
Beer, Andrew	General	£1.50
Beerts, Albert	Military	£5
Belcher, George	Comic	£4
Belet, A	Pierrotts	£8
Bem, B	Children	£12
Benois, Alexander	Various	£25
Beraud, N	Animals	£4
	Military	£5
Berkeley, Edith	General	£1
Berkeley, Stanley	Animals	£3
Berthon, Paul	Art Nouveau	£80

E. Bem, Children, Russian published £12

Bertiglia, A	Children	£8
Bianchi	Glamour	£4
Biggar, J.L.	Comic	£2
Bilibin, Ivan	Art Nouveau	£55
Billing, M	General	£1.50
Billinge, Ophelia	Animals	£5
Birch, Nora-Annie	Children	£4
Bird, H	Sport	£5
Birger	Art Deco	£18
Birtles, H.	General	£1.50
Bizuth	WW2 Comic	£3
Bjorklind, Hans	Art Deco /Sports	£12
Bjornstrom, Theodor	Fantasy	£8
Black, Algernon	Shipping	£8
Black, Montague B.	Shipping	£8
Black, W. Milne	Comic	£3
Blair, Andrew	General	£1.50
Blair, John	General	£1.50
Bob	Comic	£2
	General	£1.50
Boccasile, Gino	Art Deco	£45

Boecker, A.G.	Flowers	£1.50
Bohrdt, Hans	Shipping	£20
Boileau, Philip	Glamour	£10
Bolton, F.N.	General	£1
Bompard, S	Glamour	£6
Boriss, Margret	Children	£6
Borrow, W.H.	General	£2
Bothams, W	General	£1
Bottaro, E	Glamour	£10
Bottomley, Edwin	Animals	£3
Bottomley, George	Glamour	£3
Boulanger, Maurice	Animals	£10
	Comic	£10
Bouret, Germaine	Children	£6
Bourillon	Military	£5
Boutet, Henri	Art Nouveau	£35
Bowden, Doris	Children	£6
Bowers, Albert	General	£2
Bowers, Stephen	General	£2
Bowley, A.L.	Children	£12
Bowley M.	Animals	£6
Boyne, T	General	£1
Bradshaw, Percy V	Comic	£6
	Political	£8
Braun, W	Glamour	£6
Breanski, Arthur de	General	£2
Brett, Molly	Children	£3
Bridgeman, Arthur W	General	£2
Brisley, Nina	Children	£5
Broadrick, Jack	Comic	£2
Brown, Maynard	Glamour	£4
Browne, Stewart	Theatre	£15
Browne, Tom	Adv/Inserts	£10
	Adv/Literary	£10
	Posters	£15/£75
	Cathedrals	£6
	Comic	£4
	Theatre	£20
Brundage, Frances	Children/	
	Chromo-Litho	£15
	Others	£6
	General	£4
Brunelleschi, U	Art Deco	£100
Buchanan, Fred	Comic	£3
Buchel, Charles	Theatre	£18
Budge	Comic	£1

Bull, Rene	Comic	£4
Burger, R	General	£1
Burgess, Arthur	Shipping	£8
Burnard, Victor W.	General	£1.50
Burton, F.W.	General	£1.50
Bushby, Thomas	General	£3
Busi, Adolfo	Art Deco	£12
	Glamour	£6
Bussiere, G	Art Nouveau	£30
Butchur, Arthur	Children	£4
	Glamour	£4
Butler, G.	Animals	£2
Buxton, Dudley	Comic	£2
A.S.C.	Comic	£1.50
C.C.	Comic	£1.50
Caffieri, V	General	£2
Caldecott, Randolph	Children	£1.50
Calderara, C	Art Deco	£6
Calland, H.J.	Animals	£5
Cameron, Archie	Comic	£1.50
Cane, Ella Du	Flowers	£1.50
Capiello Leonetto	Art Nouveau	£75
Caport	Comic	£1
Carey, John	Comic	£2
Carline, George	General	£1
Carnell, Albert	Comic	£3
Carr, Paddy	Children	£2
Carrere, F.O.	Glamour	£8
Carruthers, W	General	£1.50
Carson, T.	Art Nouveau	£20
Carter, R.C.	Comic	£1.50
Carter, Reg	Comic	£1.50
	Southwold Rly.	£4
Carter, Sydney	Comic	£2
	General	£2
Cascella Basilio	General	£10
Cassiers, H	General	£6
	Royalty	£10
	Shipping	£18
Castelli, V	Children	£6
Cattley, P.R.	Comic	£2
Cauvy, Leon	Art Nouveau	£50
Cenni, Eldi	Glamour	£4
Chalker	Comic	£1.50
Chandler, E	Comic	£2

U Brunelleschi, Art Deco £100

Chapalet, Roger	Shipping	£5
Chaperon, Eugene	Military	£8
Charlet, J.A.	Glamour	£10
Chatterton, F.J.S.	Animals	£6
Cheret, Jules	Art Nouveau	£75
Cherubini, M	Glamour	£6
Chidley, Arthur	Military	£12
Chilton, G.	Art Deco	£20
Chiostri	Art Deco	£25
Christiansen, Hans	Art Nouveau	£100
Christie, G. Fyffe	Comic	£4
Christy, F. Earl	Glamour	£6
Church, Bernard, W	Shipping	£6
Clapsaddle, Ellen H.	Children	£6
	General	£4
Clarkson G.T.	Aviation	£6
Clarkson, R	General	£1
Cloke, Rene	Children	£8
Coates, A	General	£1

'Children on Moon'. Published by Degami, Series 3046 by Castelli £6

Cobbe, B	Animals	£4
Cock, Stanley	Comic	£3
Cock, Stanley	Comic	£3
Cockcroft, E.M.	UK Glamour	£6
Colbourn, Lawrence	Comic	£2
Cole, Edwin	General	£1
Coleman, W.S.	Children	£8
	General	£6
Coley, Hilda M.	Flowers	£1
Colls, H.	General	£1.50
Colombo, E.	Children	£6
	Glamour	£8
Combaz, Gisbert	Art Nouveau	£100
Comicus	Comic	£1.50
Cook, C.K.	Comic	£4
Cooper, A. Heaton	General	£1
Cooper, Phyllis	Children	£10
	Later Issues	£2
Copping, Harold	Glamour	£4
	Literary	£4
	Military	£4
Coppola, A	General	£2

Corbella, Tito	Art Deco	£18
	Glamour	£8
	Political	£8
Cordingley, G.R.	General	£1.50
Corke, C. Essenhigh	General	£2
Cottom, C.M.	Children	£5
Cowderoy, K.E.	Children	£8
	Art Deco	£18
Cowham, Hilda	Children	£8
	Comic	£6
Crackerjack	Comic	£4
Craftanara	General	£2
Craig, Janie	Flowers	£2
Cramer, Rie	Art Deco	£20
	Children	£18
Crane, Walter	Political	£18
Cremieux, Suzanne	Glamour	£8
	Military	£8
Croft, Anne	General	£1
Crombie, C.M.	Comic	£4
	Golf	£25
Cross, Roy	Comic	£4
Crow	General	£3
Croxford, W.E.	General	£1.50
Cubley, H. Hadfield	General	£1.50
Cuneo, Cyrus	Military	£8
Cynicus	Court Cards	£15
	Und. back	£5
	Landscapes	£2
	Later Comic	£2/5
	Place Names	£3
	Political	£6
	Shakespeare	£8

A Cynicus catalogue is published by Peter Stewart

J.C.D.	Comic	£1.50
J.W.D.	Comic	£1.50
Daniell, Eva	Art Nouveau	£110
Dauber	Comic	£2
Davey, George	Comic	£2
Davidson, Nora	Children	£3
Davies, Roland	Aviation	£3
Davo	Comic	£1
Daws, F.T.	Animals	£6
Dawson, Muriel	Children	£8
Dean, Frank	Sport	£4
	General	£4
Dedina, Jean	Glamour	£7
Dexter, Marjorie M.	Children	£5

Diefenbach, K.W.	Art Deco	£8
Diemer, Michael Zeno	Early ships	£12
	General	£4
Dinah	Children	£4
Dink	Sport	£8
Dirks, Gus	Comic	£4
Dixon, Charles	Shipping	£10

See feature on pages 136-137

Dobson, H.J.	General	£1.50
Docker, E. Jnr.	Art Nouveau	£60
	Animals	£5
Dodd, Francis	Military	£3
Donaldini, Jnr.	Animals	£6
Doruzhinsky, Mstislav	General	£25
Douglas, J	General	£1.50
Downey, Thos. P.	Comic	£2
Doy, H.	Comic	£1
Drallek, Yaran	Comic	£1
Drayton, Grace	See under Wiederseim	
Driscoll	Comic	£1
Drog	Glamour	£3
Drummond, Eileen	Animals	£5

Drummond, Norah	Animals	£6
Ducane, E & F	General	£1
Duddle, Josephine	Children	£8
Dudley, Tom	General	£1
Dufresne, Paul	Glamour	£5
Duncan, Hamish	Comic	£2
Duncan, J. Ellen	Children	£2
Dunk	Military	£10
Drog	Glamour	£3
Dupuis, Emile	Military	£4
Dwig	Comic	£6
Dyer, Ellen	Flowers	£1
Dyer, W.H.	General	£1
Dymond, R.J.	General	£1
E	Comic	£2
A.E.	Comic	£2
Eaman, J	General	£2
Earbalestier, C.	General	£1.50
Earnshaw, Harold	Comic	£3
Ebner, Pauli	Children	£8
Eckenbrecker, T von	Shipping	£10
Edgerton, Linda	Children	£8

Dunk, £10

Edler, Edouard	Shipping	£12
Edmunds, Kay	Military	£1.50
Edwards, Edwin	General	£1
Edwards, Lionel	Comic	£4
Eliott, Harry	Comic	£8
Elks	Comic	£1
Ellam, W.R.		
Breakfast in Bed	Comic	£10
Other Series	Comic	£10
Elliot, K.E.	Flowers	£1
Elym	Political	£5-£8
Emanuel, Frank, L.	General	£2
Endacott, S.	General	£3
Esmond,	Comic	£5
Ettwell, Elliot	General	£2
Evans, Percy	Comic	£2
A.E.F.	Children	£1
Fabian, Maud	Advertising	£15
Fabiano, F.	Glamour	£15
Fay, John H	Shipping	£4
Federley, Aleksander	Patriotic	£10
Feiertag,	Children	£3
Felix, P.E.	Art Deco	£8
Fernel, Fernand	Comic	£8
Fernoel	Art Nouveau	£8
Feure de	Art Nouveau	£160
Fidler, Alice Luella	Glamour	£8
Fidler, Elsie Catherine	Glamour	£8
Fidus, H.A. von	Art Nouveau	£60
Filby, Edgar	Advertising	£25
Finnemore, J	General	£1.50
Fisher, Harrison	Glamour	£10
Fitzgerald, A	General	£2

Elym, Political Cariacature £8

Comic Dora Eary £2.50

Fitzpatrick	Comic	£1.50
Fleury, H.	Comic	£2
	Railway	£2
Flower, Charles E.	General	£2
Folkard, Charles	Children	£15
	Literary	£15
Fontan, Leo	Glamour	£12
Forestier, A	Advertising	£35
Forres, Kit	Children	£2
Forrest, A.S.	Shipping	£3
Forsberg, J.	General	£1.50
Foster, Gilbert	General	£1.50
Foster, R.A.	General	£1.50
Fowell, G.M.	General	£1
Fradkin, E.	Children	£1.50
Francis,	General	£1
Frank, Raoul	Shipping	£18
Fraser	Comic	£1.50
Fredillo	Art Nouveau	£20
Freer, H.B.	Shipping	£8
French, Annie	Art Nouveau	£100
Fry, John H.	Shipping	£10
Fuller, Edmund	Comic	£6
	Postal	£6
Fulleylove, Joan	General	£1.50
Fullwood, A.H.	General	£5

LET'S KNOW WHEN YOU'RE
COMING AND WE'LL GET
OUT THE BAND

Kit Forres, Children £2

Furniss, Harry	Political	£5
Fych, C.D.	Glamour	£6
Gabard, E	Sport	£5
Gabb	Comic	£1.50
Gabriel, E	Shipping	£12
Gallon, R.	General	£1
Ganz	Comic	£3
Gardener, E.C.	General	£1.50
Garland, A.	General	£1.50
Gassaway, Katherine	Children	£6
Gay, Cherry	Children	£1.50
Gayac	Glamour	£15
Gear, M.	Animals	£5
Gerald, Brian	General	£1.50
Gerbault, H	Glamour	£6
Gervese, H.	Comic	£3
Gibbs, May	Comic	£25
Gibson Charles Dana	Glamour	£2
Giglio	Glamour	£5
Gilbert, Allan	Glamour	£4
Giles,	Comic	£6
Gill, Arthur	Comic	£3
Gilmour	Comic	£2.50
Gilson, T.	Comic	£2
	Military	£2
Gioja, G	General	£5
Giris	Aviation	£15

Gladwin, May	Comic	£5
Glanville	Comic	£1.50
Gobbi. D	Art Deco	£20
Goethen E. van	Children	£10
Golay, Mary	General	£3
Goodman, Maud		
/Tuck Early	Children	£18
/TuckEarly	General	£18
/Hildesheimer	Children	£4
Gotch, Phyllis, M	Comic	£2
Gould	Comic	£1.50
Govey, Lilian	Children	£8
Gozzard, J.W.	General	£1.50
Graeff	Comic	£2
Graf, Marte	Art Deco	£10
Grant, Carleton	General	£1
Grasset, Eugene	Art Nouveau	£75
Green, Alec E.	Children	£3
Green, Roland	Animals	£3
Greenall, Jack	Comic	£2
Greenaway, Kate	Children/	
	1903 printing	£65
	later printing	£15

"THEN YOU'LL REMEMBER ME"

Illustrated Songs.

Hamish, Comic, £3

Greenbank, A.	Glamour	£8
Greiner, M	Children	£10
Gresley, A.	Flowers	£1.50
Gretty, G	General	£1.50
Grey, Mollie	Children	£2
Gribble, Bernard F.	General	£2
Grimes	Comic	£3
Grin, C.U.	Comic	£1.50
Grosze, Manni	Art Deco	£10
Grunewald	Art Deco	£10
Guerzoni, C	Glamour	£8
Guggenberger, T	General	£4
Guillaume A.	Art Nouveau	£75
	Comic	£5
Gunar, Clement	Easter Witches.	£10
Gunn, A.	Glamour	£5
Gunn Gwennet	Comic	£2
Gurnsey, C.	Comic	£1.50
Guy, T.	General	£1
E.A.H.	Comic	£1.50
F.W.H.	Comic	£3
S.H.	Comic	£1
Hager, Nini	Art Nouveau	£80
Hailey, Edward	General	£1
Haller, A.	Flowers	£2
Halliday	Comic	£3
Hamilton, E	Shipping	£8
Hamilton, J.M.	Sport	£18
Hamish	Comic	£2
Hammick, J.W.	Glamour	£3
Hammond, J.	Flowers	£1.50
Hampel, Walter	Art Nouveau	£85
Hanbury, F. Schmidt	General	£1.50

Hannaford	General	£1.50
Hansi	Children	£15
	Political	£15
Harbour, Jennie	Art Deco	£15
Hardy, Dudley	Comic	£6
	Glamour	£9
	Political	£12
	Shipping	£20
	Theatre	£20
Hardy, Florence	Children	£6
Hardy, F.	Art Deco	£10
Hardy, F.C.	Military	£4
Harriet	Comic	£1
Harrison, E. Florence	Glamour	£6
Hart, Josef	Art Nouveau	£35
Hartridge, Norman	Children	£10
Harvey, F.	Comic	£1.50
Haslehust, E.W.	General	£1.50
Hassall, John	Comic	£5
	Court Size	£15
	Theatre	£30
	General	£4
Hauby, S.	Art Nouveau	£12
Haviland, Frank	Glamour	£5
Hayes, F.W.	General	£1.50
Hayes, Sydney	Animals	£1.50
Hebblethwaite, S.H.	Comic	£3
Heinirch	General	£6
Henckel, Carl	Military	£6
Henley	Comic	£1.50
Henley, W.E.	General	£1.50
Henry, Thomas	Children	£6
	Comic	£6
Herouard	Glamour	£15
Herrfurth, Oskar	Children	£10
Heusser, Harry	Shipping	£8
Hey, Paul	General	£4
Heyermanns,S.	General	£1.50
Heyermans, John A	General	£1.50
Hickling, P.B.	General	£1.50
Hier, Prof. van	General	£1.50
Higham, Sydney	General	£1.50
Hiles, Bartram	General	£2
Hill, L. Raven	Political	£5
Hilton, Alf	Comic	£2

Mary Hill, art views £3

A Humourist in France. *After the black & white drawing by Dudley Hardy.*
LIGHT AND AIRY.

Dudley hardy, Comic £5

Hines, B.	General	£1..50
Hodgson, W. Scott	General	£1
Hofer, Andre	Glamour	£7
Hoffman, H.W.	General	£1
Hoffman, J.	Art Nouveau	£90
Hoffmann, Anton	Military	£8
Hohenstein, A	Art Nouveau	£35
Hohlwein, Ludwig	Advertising	£25
	Military	£10
Holloway, Edgar A.	Military	£12
Hollyer, Eva	Children	£8
Home, Gordon	General	£1.50
Hood, Eileen	Animals	£4
Hopcroft, G.E.	General	£1.50
Hopking, Noel	Animals	£1
Horder, Margaret	Children	£2
Horrell, Charles	Glamour	£4
Horsfall, Mary	Children	£6
	Glamour	£4
Horwitz, Helena	Glamour	£4
Howard, C.T.	General	£1.50
Howard, Jim	Comic	£1.50
Howell, E.	Comic	£1.50
Hudson, Gerald	Military	£4
Hughes, Alun	Comic	£1.50

Hughes, Lloyd	Comic	£1.50
Hughes, R.	General	£1
Hummel	Children	£4
Hunt, Edgar	Animals	£2
Hunt, Muriel	Animals	£4
Hunter, Mildred C	Animals	£4
Hurst, Hal	Comic	£3
Hutchinson, F.	General	£1
Hyde, Graham	Comic	£6
Ibbetson, Ernest	Comic	£8
	Military	£12
Icart, Louis	Glamour	£12
Innes, John	General	£2
Inskip, J. Henry	General	£1.50
Iranez, J	Children	£4
Ironico	Comic	£1.50
Irwin	Comic	£1
J.R.J.	Comic	£1.50
Jackson, Helen	Children	£18
Jackson, Ian	Glamour	£5
Jacobs, Helen	Children	£8
Jafuri, R.	General	£3
James, Frank	Animals	£1.50
James, Ivy Millicent	Children	£10
Jank, Angelo	Art Nouveau	£35
Jarach, A	Glamour	£12
Jaderholm-Snellman, Greta-Lisa		
	Art Deco / Glamour	£15
Jay, Cecil	Glamour	£5
Jenkins, G.H.	General	£1.50
Jester	Comic	£1.50
Jo	Comic	£1
Johnson, M.	General	£1.50
Johnson, S.	General	£1.50
Jossot	Art Nouveau	£160
Josza, Carl	Art Nouveau	£60
Jotter	Comic Types	£3
	Greetings	£2
	Hotels	£3/10
	Derbys/Cornwall	£1
	Sheffield/Ireland	£4
	Views -Other	£2
Jung, Maurice	Art Nouveau	£500
A.H.K.	General	£1
C.K.	Comic	£1.50

E.M.T.K.	Comic	£1.50
Kaby	Glamour	£4
Kainradl, L	Art Nouveau	£100
Kammerer, Rob	General	£1.50
Karaktus	Comic	£1.50
Kaskeline, Fred	Children	£6
Katinka	Art Deco	£12
Kaufmann, J.C.	Animals	£2
Keene, Elmer	General	£1.50
Keene, Frank	Comic	£1.50
Keene, Minnie	Animals	£2
Keesey, Walter M.	General	£1
Kempe	Children	£6
Kennedy, A.E.	Animals	£6
	Comic	£6
	Theatre	£12
Kerr, Tom	Children	£1
Kid	Comic	£1.50
Kidd, Will	Children	£6
Kieszkow	Art Nouveau	£30
Kimball, Alonzo	Glamour	£5
King A. Price	General	£1.50
King, Edward	General	£3
King, Gunning	General	£3
King, Jessie M.	Art Nouveau	£85
King, W.B.	Comic	£1.50
King, Yeend	General	£1.50
Kinnear, J.	General	£2
Kinsella, E.P.	Children	£6
	Comic	£6
	Theatre	£20
Kircher, A.	Naval	£4
Kirchner, Raphael		

Mela Koehler, Art Deco £70

/Early Art Nouveau		£50 - £100
/WW1 period	Glamour	£30
/Bruton Galleries	Glamour	£25
Kirk, A.H.	General	£1.50
Kirkbach	Children	£3
Kirkpatrick	General	£1
Kirmse, Persis	Animals	£5
Klein, Christina	General/	
	Chromo-Litho	£6
	Later Issues	£3
Kley, Paul	Chromo-Litho	£6
	Other printings	£2
Klodic	Shipping	£6
Knox, W	General	£1.50
Koch, Ludwig	Sport	£6
Koehler, Mela	Art Deco	£70
	Art Nouveau	£120
Koehler Mela Broman	Art Deco	£25
Kokoschka	Art Nouveau	£600
Konopa	Art Nouveau	£35
Kosa	Art Nouveau	£100
Koy	Comic	£1.50
Kulas, J.V.	Art Nouveau	£35
Kupka	Art Nouveau	£75
Kyd	Comic	£8
	Literary	£12
	London Life	£10
Lacy, Chas J.de	Shipping	£12
Lajoux, Edmond	Military	£5
Lamb, Eric	General	£1
Lambert, H.G.C. Marsh	Children	£5
Lancere, Yergenyi	General	£15
Lang, W.	Art Nouveau	£35
Larcombe, Ethel	Art Nouveau	£35
Lasalle, Jean	Glamour	£2
	General	£2
Laskoff F	Art Nouveau	£50
Lauder, C.J.	General	£1.50
Lautrec, H. de Toulouse	Art Nouveau	£600
Lawes, H.	General	£1
Laz	Comic	£1.50
Leete, Alfred	Comic	£4
Leggatt, C.P.	Comic	£2
Lehmann, Felix	Sport	£6
Lehmann, Phil	Comic	£2

F.G.Lewin, Comic £4

Leigh, Conrad	Military	£4
Lelee Leopold	Art Nouveau	£60
LeMunyon, Pearl Fidler	Glamour	£6
Leng, Max	Art Nouveau	£30
Leodud Di	Art Deco	£6
Leonnec, G.	Glamour	£15
Leroux Pierre Albert	Military	£5
Leroy	Military	£5
Lesker, H.	Art Deco	£8
Lessieux, E. Louis	Art Nouveau	£40
	Shipping	£25
Lester, Adrienne	Animals	£3
Lester, Ralph	Glamour	£3
Lewin, F.G.	Children	£6
	Comic	£4
Lilien, E.M.	Art Nouveau	£40
	General	£8
Lime, H.	Comic	£1
Lindsay, J.	General	£1
Lindsell, L.	Glamour	£3
Livemont, Privat	Art Nouveau	£100
Lloyd, T. Ivester	Glamour	£4
	Military	£5
Loffler Berthold	Art Nouveau	£100
Loffler, Lovat	Art Nouveau	£30
Loir Luigi	General	£6
Long, L.M.	General	£1.50
Longley, Chilton	Art Deco	£35
Longmire, R.O.	Political	£10
Longstaffe, Ernest	General	£1.50
Loreley	Art Deco	£15
Lorenz, Fabius	Glamour	£10

Love, H. Montagu	Military	£6
	General	£2
Lovering, I.	General	£1.50
Lowe, Meta	Children	£2
Luckcott G.Y.	Comic	£1.50
Ludgate	Comic	£2
Ludlow, Hal	Comic	£2
Ludovici, A.	Children	£5
	Comic	£3
	Political	£3
Luke W.	Comic	£2
Lumley, Savile	Military	£4
Lynen, Amedee	General	£4
C.M.	Comic	£1
M.S.M.	Glamour	£15
P.C.M.	Comic	£1.50
Mac/National Series	Comic	£2
Mac	Animals	£5
	Comic	£3
MacBean L.C.	Comic	£2
McGill, Donald	Comic/ Early Dated	£8
	Pre-1914	£5
	1914-1939	£3-6
	'New'	£1
McIntyre, J.	General	£1.50
McIntyre, R.F.	General	£1.50
McNeill, J.	Military	£12
Macdonald, A.K.	Art Nouveau	£35
Mackain, F.	Comic	£3
Macleod, F.	Comic	£2
Macpherson, John	General	£1
MacWhirter, J.	General	£1.50
Maggs, J.C.	Coaching	£2

Donald McGill, Comic 1914-1939 £3

Maguire, Bertha	General	£1.50
Maguire, Helena	Animals	£8
	General	£3
Mailick, A.	Glamour	£4
	General	£3
Mainzer, Alfred	Animals	£3
Mair, H. Willebeek le	Children	£6
Mallet, Beatrice	Children	£5
Mallet, Dennis	Comic	£1.50
Manavian, V.	Comic	£3
Mann, James S	Shipping	£12
Marchant, Leslie P.	Comic	£1.50
Marco, M.	Glamour	£3
Marechaux, C.	Glamour	£4
Margetson, Hester	Children	£5
Marisch, G.	Art Nouveau	£75
Maroc	Comic	£1
Marshall, Alice	Children	£12
Mart	Comic	£1.50
Martin, E	Children	£8
Martin, L.B.	Comic	£3
	Children	£5

Midge, WW2 Humour £5

Martin, Phil	Comic	£2
Martineau, Alice	Glamour	£8
	General	£3
	Children	£8
Martini, A.	Adverts	£35
	Political	£25
Martino R. de	General	£1
Marty, Andre	Art Deco	£15
Mason, Finch	Comic/Sport	£4
Mason, Frank H.	Shipping	£5
Mason, George W	Comic	£4
Mastroianni, D.	General	£2
Mataloni, G.	Art Nouveau	£30
Matthison, W.	General	£1.50
Maurice, Reg	Comic	£2
Mauzan, A.	Children	£6
	Glamour	£10
	Political	£6
	Art Deco	£20
	General	£3
May, F.S.	Comic	£2
May, J.A.	Comic	£2
May, Phil	Comic/	
	Write-away	£8
	Oilette	£4
Maybank, Thomas	Children	£12
Mayer, Lou	Glamour	£5
Meadows, Chas	Comic	£2
Menpes, Mortimer	Children	£3
Meras, Rene	Glamour	£7
Mercer, Joyce	Art Deco	£25
	Children	£25
Meredith, Jack	Comic	£2
Merte, O.	Animals	£5
Meschini, G.	Art Deco	£35

E. Martin, Girl skiing £8

Metlicovitz, L.	Art Nouveau	£35
Meunier, Henri	Art Nouveau	£95
Meunier, Suzanne	Glamour	£20
Mich	Comic	£1.50
Midge	Comic	£5
Mignot, Victor	Art Nouveau	£35
Mike	Comic	£1
Miller, Hilda T.	Children/	
	Liberty	£15
	Other Pubs.	£8
Miller, Laurence.	Humour	£4-£6
	Tennis	£15
Milliere, Maurice	Glamour	£15
Millor	Flowers	£1
Millot	Greetings	£1
Mills, Ernest, H.	Animals	£4
Monestier, C.	Glamour	£6
Monier, Maggy	Glamour	£10
Moore, A. Winter	General	£1.50
Moore, F.	Railway	£3
Montague, Love, H	Military	£8
Montague, R.	Shipping	£6
	General	£1.50
Montedoro, M	Art Deco	£50
Moreland, Arthur	Comic	£3
	Political	£5
Morgan, F.E.	Comic	£3
Morris, M.	General	£1.50
Morrow, Albert	Theatre	£12
Moser, Koloman	Art Nouveau	£120
Mostyn, Dorothy	Glamour	£4
Mostyn, Marjorie	Glamour	£4
Mouton, G.	Glamour	£10

"Destroyer and Submarine"

F.E. Morgan £3

Mucha, Alphonse	Art Nouveau	£100+
	Exhibition	£100
	Slav Period	£50
Muggiai	Glamour	£15
Mulholland, S.A.	General	£1
Muller, A.	Animals	£4
Muller, Valery	General	£8
Muraton, E.	Flowers	£2
Murhaghan Kathleen, I.	Children	£4
Musta, Ville	Ethnic	£3- £6
Mutter, K.	General	£4

God Jul och Gott Nytt År
tillönskas av
NERMAN

Nerman, Art Deco £18

H. Meunier, Glamour £95

Naillod, C.S.	Glamour	£6
Nam, Jacques	Glamour	£10
Nanni, G.	Glamour	£6
Nap	Comic	£2
Nash, A.A.	Children	£4
Nerman	Art Deco	£18
	Theatre	£25
Neumont, M	Glamour	£5
Neville-Cumming, R	Shipping	£8
Newton, G.E.	General	£1.50
Ney	Glamour	£10
Nicholson, J	Shipping	£5
Nielsen, Harry B.	Comic	£2
Nielsen, Vivienne	Animals	£3
Nixon, K.	Children	£10
Noble, Ernest	Comic	£3
Norfield, Edgar	Comic	£1.50
Norman, Parsons	General	£1.50
Norman, Val	General	£1.50
Norwood, A.Harding	General	£1.50
Noury, Gaston	Art Nouveau	£80
Nystrom, Jenny	Children	£12
	Glamour	£12

L.Peltier Glamour £8

Jenny Nystrom Children £12

O'Beirne, F.	Military	£12
O'Kay	Comic	£1
O'Neill, Rose	Children	£8
Operti, A.	General	£5
Opper, F.	Comic	£1.50
Orens, Denizard	Political	£18
Ost. A.	Art Nouveau	£30
Ostrumova-Lebeva, A	General	£25
Outcault, R.F.	Children	£8
	Comic	£5
Outhwaite, Ida R.	Children	£25
Overell, J.	Children	£4
Overnell	Children	£5
Owen, Will	Comic	£4
	Theatre	£12
Oyston, George	General	£1.50
Paget, Wal	General	£1.50
Paischeff, Alexander	Finnish Views	£5
Palmer, Phyllis, M.	Children	£5
Palmer, Sutton	General	£1.50
Pannett, R.	Glamour	£8
	Theatre	£18
Parker, N.	Animals	£4
Parkinson, Ethel	Children	£5

Harry Payne, Metropolitan Police £40

Parlett, Harry	Comic	£1.50
Parlett, T.	Comic	£2
Parr, B.F.C.	General	£1
Parr, Doreen	Children	£4
Partridge, Bernard	Political	£4
Parsons, F.J.	Railway	£3
Patek, August	Art Nouveau	£12
Patella, B.	Art Nouveau	£35
Paterson, Vera	Children	£3
Paulus	Military	£3
Payne, Arthur C	General	£2
Payne, G.M.	Comic	£3
	Glamour	£3
Payne, Harry		
/Tuck Early	Horses	£40
/Tuck Early	Military	£40
/Metropolitan Police	General	£40
/Wild West	General	£30
/Coaching	Animals	£30
/Gale & Polden	Military	£15
/Stewart & Woolf	Military	£15
/Badges & Wearers	Military	£12+
/Oilettes	Horses	£6
/Oilettes	Military	£6+
/Military in London	Military	£4
/Rural Life	General	£5
/Other	General	£10+
Pears, Chas	Advertising	£15

Pearse, Susan B	Children	£12
Peddie, Tom	Glamour	£3
Pellegrini, E.	Glamour	£18
Peltier, L.	Glamour	£8
Penley, Edwin A.	General	£1.50
Pennington, Oswald	Shipping	£7
Penny, Theo	Comic	£1.50
Penot, A.	Glamour	£15
Pepin, Maurice	Glamour	£12
Peras	Glamour	£8
Percival, E.D.	General	£1.50
Perlberg, F.	Animals	£4
	General	£1.50
Perly	Comic	£1.50
Person, Alice Fidler	Glamour	£6
Petal	Comic	£1
Peterson, Hannes	General	£2
Pfaff, C.	General	£6
Philippi, Robert	Art Nouveau	£15
Phillimore, R.P.	General	£4
Phipson, E.A.	General	£1.50
Phiz	Dickens	£5
Pike, Sidney	General	£1.50

Maurice Pepin £12

Pillard,	Glamour	£6
	Military	£6
Pinder, Douglas	General	£1
Pingers	Political	£6
Pinhey, Edith	General	£1
Pinkawa, Anton	Art Nouveau	£30
Piper, George	Children	£3
Pirkis	Comic	£3
Pitcher, Henrie	General	£3
Pizer, Herbert	Glamour	£8
Plumstead, Joyce	Children	£8
Pohola, Jouko	Helsinki Olympics £12	
Polzin, G.	General	£4
Pope, Dorothy T.	Animals	£8
Popini	Art Nouveau	£30
	Glamour	£5
Poulbot, Francisque	Children	£4
Poy	Comic	£1.50
Praga, Alfred	Shipping	£12
Presland, A.L.	Flowers	£1.50
Preston, Chloe	Children	£9
Prosnocimi, A.	General	£1.50
Purser, Phyllis	Children	£4
Pyp	Comic	£2
Quatremain, W.W.	General	£1.50
Quinnell, Cecil W.	Glamour	£4
	Literary	£4
Quinton, A.R.		
/Salmon J. & Co.	South Africa	£12+
	Ostende	£15+
	General	£3 +
	1960/70 Period	.75
	Reprints/7 digit computer nos.	.25

Xavier Sager, Glamour £15

/Tuck R. & Sons	General	£4+
Quinton, F.E.	General	£1.50
Quinton, Harry	Comic	£2
Quips	Comic	£1.50
A.F.R.	Comic	£1.50
F.A.R.	General	£1.50
J.S.R.	Comic	£1.50
Rackham, Arthur	Children	£25
Raemaekers, Louis	Political	£3
Ralph, Lester	Glamour	£6
Raimondi, R.	General	£3
Rambler	General	£1
Ramsey, George S.	General	£1
Rankin, George	Animals	£3
Rappini	Glamour	£5
	General	£4
Ratcliffe, W.W.	General	£4
Rauh, Ludwig	Glamour	£15
Raven, Phil.	Comic	£1.50
Read, F.W.	Glamour	£3
	General	£1
Read, T. Buchanan	General	£1
Reckling, L.G.	General	£1
Reichert, C.	Animals	£4
Reiss, Fritz	General	£5
Remington Frederick	General	£8
Renaud, M.	Flowers	£1
Renault, A.	Flowers	£1
Rennie, M.	General	£1.50
Rex	Comic	£1
Reynolds, Frank	Comic	£4
	Literary	£5
Ribas	Glamour	£10
Richardson, Agnes	Children	£5
Richardson, Charles	Comic	£1.50
Richardson, R.V.	Comic	£2
Richardson, R.W.E.	General	£1.50
Richmond, Leonard	Railways	£10
Rickard, J.	Children	£8
Right	Comic	£2
Riley,W.E.	Military	£3
Ritchie, Alick P.F.	Comic	£3
Ritter, Paul	General	£4
Robert, Lucien	Glamour	£15

G.E.Shepheard, Comic, £5

	Misc.	£5
Rust, A.	Comic	£1.50
Ryan, F.	Comic	£1.50
Ryland, Henry	Glamour	£8
Rylander	Art Deco	£15-£25
S. (Capital)	Comic	£1.50
S. (Script)	Comic	£1.50
J.M.S.	Comic	£1.50
K.S.	Comic	£1.50
M.S.	Children	£1.50
S.E.S.	Comic	£1.50
Sachetti, E.	Political	£8
Sager, Xavier	Glamour	£15
Salaman, Edith	General	£5
Salmony, G.	Glamour	£5
Samokiche, N	Military	£15
Sancha, F.	Political	£8
Sand, Adina	Glamour	£54
Sanders, A.E.	General	£1.50
Sanderson, Amy	Children	£3
Sandford, H.Dix	Children	£6

Roberts, Howard L.	Comic	£2
Roberts, Violet M	Animals	£20
	Comic	£20
Rob, G.	Comic/Patriotic	£5
Robida, A.	General	£5
Robinson, W. Heath	Comic	£6
Rodella, G.	Glamour	£5
Rog	Comic	£1.50
Romney, George	Railways	£3
Rooke, H.K.	Shipping	£10
Rose, Freda Mabel	Children	£3
Rosenvinge, Odin	Shipping	£12
Rossi, J.C.	Art Nouveau	£65
Rostro	Political	£15
Rousse, Frank	General	£2
Rowland, Ralph	Comic	£2
Rowlandson, G.	Military	£5
	Comic	£3
	General	£1.50
Rowntree, Harry	Animals	£12
	Comic	£12
Rubino, Antonio	Advertising	£30
	Children	£4
	Patriotic	£8

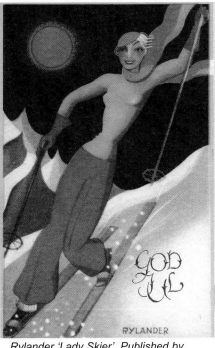

Rylander 'Lady Skier'. Published by
Axel Eliassons, Stockholm £25.00

	Black Humour	£8
Sandy-Hook	Shipping	£12
Sarg, Tony	Comic	£2
Sartoi, E.	General	£1
Sauber	General	£6
	Social History	£6
Saville Rena	Children	£1.50
Sayer, Henry	Comic	£5
Schiele, Egon	Art Nouveau	£100+
Schiesl, R.	General	£3
Schmidt-Hamburg	Shipping	£10
	General	£1.50
Schonflug, Fritz	Comic	£4
Schonian	Animals	£4
Schubert, H.	Glamour	£5
Schweiger, L.	General	£4
Scottie	Glamour	£6
Scribbler	Comic	£1.50
Scrivener, Maude	Animals	£3
Severn, Walter	General	£1.50
Sgrilli	Children	£5
Shand, C.E.	Art Deco	£10
Shaw, H.G.	Animals	£6

THE TREATY WITH JAPAN.

G. Rob, Patriotic £5

Shaw, W. Stocker	Comic	£2
Shelton, S.	General	£1.50
Shepheard, G.E.	Comic	£5
Sherrin, A.	General	£1.50
Sherwin, D.	General	£1
Shmerling, Oscar	General	£7
Shoesmith, Kenneth	Shipping	£12
Short, E.A.	Flowers	£1.50
Sikes, F.H.	General	£1.50
Simkin, R.	Military	£15
Simonetti, A.M.	Glamour	£5
Sinty, Juan	Comic	£1.50
Skip	Comic	£1
Smale, B.H.	Comic	£8
	Military	£8
Small, D.	General	£2
Smith D. Carlton	Children	£5
Smith, Edna	Children	£2
Smith, Jessie Wilcox	Art Nouveau	£35
	Children	£30
Smith, May	Children	£8
Smith, Syd	Comic	£2

Hans C Starke,   £10

64

MR. AUSTEN CHAMBERLAIN, M.P.

He has had many advantages, no doubt ; but, apart from all these he is a young man of agreeable presence, real ability, and much promise. It is hard to look unaffected behind an eyeglass and an orchid, and yet he is an unaffected young man.

Spy, Political, £15

Smith, W.	General	£1.50
Smyth	Comic	£1
Sokolov, Yevgeni	General	£10
Solomko, Serge de	Glamour	£20
Somerville, Howard	Glamour	£4
	Comic	£2
Sonrel, Elizabeth	Art Nouveau	£50/60
Sowerby, Millicent	Children/	
	Chromo-Litho	£20
	Other types	£8
Spatz	Comic	£2
Sperlich, T.	Animals	£6
Spindler, Erwin	General	£6
Spurgin, Fred	Comic	£3
	Glamour	£5
	Military	£5
Spurrier, W.B.	Comic	£2
Spy	Political	£15
Stanlaw, S. Penrhyn	Glamour	£4
Stanlaws, Penly	Glamour	£6
Stannard, H. Sylvester	General	£2
Stannard, Lilian	General	£2
Stark, Han C	Art Deco	£10
Stassen, F	Music	£15

Stead, A.	General	£1
Steele, L.	Children	£4
Steinlen, Alexandre	Art Nouveau	£90
Stenberg, Aina	Art Deco	£15
Sternberg, V.W.	Children	£2
Stewart, J.A.	Animals	£5
	Military	£5
Stoddart, R.W.	Comic	£2
Stokes G. Vernon	Animals	£2
Stone, Frederick	Comic	£1.50
Stone, F.	Comic	£2
Stower, Willi	Shipping/	
	Early	£20
	Later	£8
	General	£6
Stretton, Philip	Animals	£5
Strom, Bjorn	Art Deco	£8
Strong, G.W.	Comic	£1.50
Studdy, G.E.	Comic/	
	Bonzo	£8
	Others	£6
Sullivan, Pat	Comic	£5
Syd	Comic	£2
Syllikuss	Comic	£2

Millicent Sowerby, Children £8

Lance Thackeray, Oilette £6

Symonds, Constance	Children	£8
Szyk, Arthur	Political	£6/£15
T.	Comic	£1
C.T.	Comic	£1.50
J.T.	General	£1.50
L.B.T.	Comic	£1.50
W.E.T.	Comic	£1.50
Tait	Comic	£1
Talboys, A.	Animals	£3
Tam, Jean	Glamour	£12
Tanquerey, L.	Art Deco	£4
Tarrant, Margaret W.	Children/6	
	Pre-1945	£6
	1945 on	£2
Taylor, A.	Children	£1.50
	Comic	£1.50
Taylor, E.S.	Comic	£1.50
Tempest, Douglas	Children	£1.50
	Comic	£1.50
Tempest, Margaret	Children	£3
Terzi, A.	Glamour	£8
Thackeray, Lance	Comic/Cricket	£15
	Write-away	£10
	Oilettes	£5
Theo	Aviation	£20

Thiede, Adolf	General	£1.50
Thiele, Arthur	Animals	£15+
	Comic	£15+
	Political	£25
Thomas, Bert	Comic	£5
Thomas, Paul	Animals	£5
Thomas, Victor	Children	£6
Thomas, Walter	Shipping	£10
Thompson, E.H.	General	£1.50
Thorne, Diana	Animals	£1.50
Titicus	Comic	£1.50
Toussaint, M.	Military	£6
Travis, Stuart	General	£1.50
Trick, E.W.	General	£1.50
Tringham, H.	General	£1.50
Trow	Comic	£1
True, W.	Theatre	£12
Truman, Herbert	General	£1
Tuhka, Aukusti	Art Deco / Glam	£8- £12
Turner, C.E.	Shipping	£8
Turrian, E.D.	Art Nouveau	£30
Twelvetrees, C.H.	Children	£6
Uden, E.	General	£1
Ullman, Max	Shipping	£15
Underwood, Clarence F	Glamour	£6
Upton, Florence K.	Children	£35
Usabal, Luis	Glamour	£10/15
Utrillo, A.	General	£6
Valles, F.	Comic	£1.50
Vallet, L.	Glamour	£10
	Military	£4
Valter, Eugenie M.	Animals	£4
Valter, Florence E.	Animals	£4
Vaughan, E.H.	General	£1.50
Veal, O.	Comic	£2
Vera	Children	£2
Vernon, E.	Glamour	£6
Vernon, R.W.	General	£1.50
Villon Jacques	Art Nouveau	£300
Voellmy, F.	General	£8
Vouga, E.	Flowers	£1
F.W.	Comic	£1.50
J.S.W.	Comic	£2
Maurice Wagemans	*Military*	*£3*
Wain, Louis	Animals/Early	£60+
	Later	£40+
	Oilettes	£40+
	Advertising	£75+

(*For a more comprehensive listing of Louis Wain cards, please refer to page 23*

Wal.	Comic	£1.50
Walbourn, Ernest	General	£1.50
Walker, F.S.	General	£1.50
Walker, Hilda	Animals	£4
Wanke, Alice	Art Nouveau	£20
	Children	£10
Ward, Dudley	Comic	£3
Ward, Herbert	Military	£5
Ward, Vernon	General	£1.50
Wardle, Arthur	Animals	£8
Warrington, Ellen	General	£1.50
Watson, C.M. West	Animals	£5
Wealthy, R.J.	Animals	£3
Weaver, E.	Comic	£1.50
Webb, A.D.	General	£1
Weierter, Louis	Advertising	£25
Welzi, A.	Art Nouveau	£30
Wennerberg, Brynolf	Art Nouveau	£20
	Glamour	£15
West, A.L.	Animals	£2
West, Reginald	General	£1.50
Weston, Rita F.	Children	£1
Whatley, H	General	£2
Wheeler, Dorothy	Children	£4
Whishaw, A.Y.	General	£1.50
White, Brian	Children	£2
	Comic	£2
White, D.	Comic	£2
White, Flora	Children	£5
White, H. Percy	Comic	£2
Whitehead, Fred	General	£1.50
Wichera, R.R.	Children	£6
	Glamour	£8
Wiederseim, G.G.	Children	£6
Wielandt, Manuel	General	£5
Wilcock, A.M.	Children	£4
Wilkin, Bob	Comic	£1
Wilkinson, Gilbert	Comic	£5
Wilkinson, Norman	Shipping	£10
Williams, Madge	Children	£3
Williams, Warren	General	£1.50
Willis, George	Comic	£1.50
Wilson, David	Political	£6

Flora White, Children £6

Wimble, Arthur	Glamour	£2
Wimbush, Henry B.	General	£2
Wimbush, Winifred	General	£3
	Glamour	£6
Wishaw, M.C.	General	£3
Wood, Lawson	Comic	£6
	Gran'pop	£5
	Theatre	£18
Wood, Starr	Comic	£5
Woodville, R. Caton	Military	£6
Woollett, Cress	Glamour	£3
Woude Sikko van de	General	£2
Wright, Gilbert	General	£4
Wright, Seppings,	General	£2
Wuyts, A	Children	£6
	Glamour	£6
Wyllie, W.L.	Shipping	£8
H.Y.	Comic	£1.50
Young, A.	General	£1.50
Young Gwen Hayward	General	£3
Young, Hayward	General	£3
Zandrino, Adelina	Glamour	£10
Zirka, C.	Glamour	£6

THE SYMBOL of VICTORY

RIGHT o'er the world
this symbol appears,
Predicting the passing
of terror and fears;
Speaking of VICTORY
well on the way;
Hailing the dawn
of a happier day.
When Liberty, Justice
and Freedom again

men

Junior.

A BRITISH AIR PILOT
Preparing for a night
bombing raid

THE

It is 70 years since the Battle
Britain in September 1940 , I

WATCH ADOLF TREMBLE. SISTER!

WATS

FEW

ve have a few of the patriotic
ards published at the time...

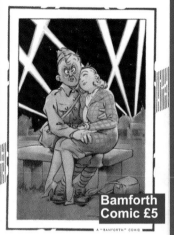

WHO WANTS
BLINKING SEARCHLIGHTS
TO-NIGHT?

Bamforth
Comic £5

A "BAMFORTH" COMIC

The Spirit
of
Britain

Patriotic
WW2 £8

We shall go on to the end....We shall
fight in France, we shall fight on the seas and
in the oceans, shall fight with growing con-
fidence and growing strength in the air.. We
shall defend our island, whatever the cost may
be. We shall fight on the beaches, we shall fight
on the landing grounds, we shall fight in the fields
and streets and in the hills.... We shall never
surrender, and even if, which I do not for a
moment believe, this island, or even part of it, is
subjugated and starving, then our Empire across
the seas, armed and guarded by the British Fleet,
will carry on the struggle, until, in God's good
time, the new world, in all its strength and might,
sets forth to the rescue and liberation of
the old. Britain will fight the menace of tyranny
for years, and, if necessary, alone.
— Winston Churchill

VICKERS-SUPERMARINE "SPITFIRE IX"
1-Rolls-Royce "Merlin 61" Engine

Flight published
Photographic issue £4

AVIATION

The early days of flying presented a challenge which postcard publishers were not slow to take up, with the resulting legacy of a great many fine studies both photographic and artistic on this theme. Postcards cover the whole spectrum of civil and military aviation from the early beginnings, through World War I to the nineteen-thirties and up to the present day. Generally speaking photographic cards are worth more than artistic studies, the former often having some related local history interest. It must be further emphasised that in all cases prices given are for unused cards. If postally used a much higher figure may be expected, depending upon type of postmark, date of flight, clarity of strike etc.

Market Report:
Some of the early air races are starting to attract interest. Modern civil aviation has produced some high prices on the internet for smaller and unusual airline issues.

AIRCRAFT

AIRCRAFT Pre-1918

Flying at Hendon Series	£15-£20
Brooklands Aviation	£20
Daily Mail Tour 1912	£10
At named locations	£30
French Aviation	£10
Civil aircraft	£10
Military aircraft	£8

Accidents

Identified	£25
Unidentified	£5

Series

Lefebvre Utile	£35
Lombart	£25

Educational Series

Tuck R. & Sons	£20

The Lightning Series

E. Cook	£15

Famous Aeroplane Series

Tuck R. & Sons	£5

In the Air Series

Tuck R. & Sons	£6

Artist/Derek Bannister

Salmon J. Ltd	£5

AIRCRAFT 1918-1939

Schneider Trophy	£20+
Civil Aircraft	£10-15
Military Aircraft	£5-10
Joy Flights	£6-8

Accidents

Identified	£25
Unidentified	£5

Amy Johnson

England-Australia Flight/Set 6/	
Tuck R. & Sons/3867B	£15
Portraits	£15

Imperial Airways

Croydon Airport	£18
Official	£18
Pilots	£20

AIRCRAFT 1939 - 1960

Civil Aircraft	£8-15

Real Photograph Series

Valentine	£3

PILOTS

Pre-1914

With aircraft	£15
Portraits	£12

1918-1939

With aircraft	£15
Portraits	£12

Flying at Hendon showing the crowd at an early meeting, easily worth £18

A Macchi "52" acheived 260 Mph in a Schneider Trophy race £20

French Aviation series £10

Charles Lindburgh with Spirit of St Louis £30

Rouen Aviation Meeting Poster Advert £60

Schneider Trophy Poster type £25

Bournemouth meeting   £25

Tuck educational series £20

Flying at Hendon series £20

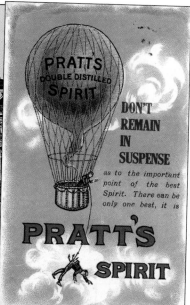

Poster advert for Pratt's motor spirit £60

'Le Brix' R/P £12

Airfield, Paris-Orly £10

Commercial airline, by Bannister £5

Wright Biplane, Pau 1909 £35

DH Daedalus, Salmon £5

AVIATION MEETINGS

Blackpool 1909/10	£20
Doncaster 1909	£30
Bournemouth 1910	£25
Burton on Trent 1910	£40
Lanark 1910	£40
Wolverhampton 1910	£40

AIRSHIPS

At named locations	£30
World Flights	£25
GB/Pre-1918	
Barton Airship/Alexandra Palace 1905	£35
Beta/Gamma/Parseval etc.	£18
GB/1918-1939	
R-100/R-101 etc.	£18
French/German	
Pre-1918	£15
1918-1939	£15
Zeppelins	
Early Chromo embossed etc.	£25+
World War 1/ Close-up	£18
/Combat sketches	£5
Wreckage/GB Locations	£10

First Aerial post 1911 London-Windsor Flown and postmarked London £30

Poster Adverts

Coloured	£60
Black & White	£30
Early Airline Poster Adverts	£85

Zeppelin wreckage in UK £10

FLOWN CARDS

Beckenham Coronation Balloon/9.8.02
Flown
Unflown

Lifeboat Saturday/20.9.02

Flown	£1,000
Unflown	£100

Lifeboat Saturday/29.8.03

Flown	£1,000
Unflown	£100

Daily Graphic Expedition 1907

Flown	£150
Unflown	£50

First U.K. Aerial Post 1911

London-Windsor - Flown	£20/£40
Windsor-London - Flown	£30/£75
Unflown cards	£18

N.B. The value of flown U.K. Aerial Post Cards depends upon which colour type has been used, date of flight, clarity of strike etc. These factors are also relevant to any flown cards.

BALLOONS

At named locations	£65
Photographic	£35+
Printed	£20
Military/Printed	£8
Swiss/Meetings Posters	£75+

MISCELLANEOUS

Airfields	£8-12
R.F.C. Interest	£5-8

Commemorative Cards

First/Historic Flights	£25+

Croydon Airport

C.H. Price Series	£20

Royal Air Force

Halton Camp	£8
Airmen/Photographs Identified	£5
/Unidentified	£1.50
Miscellaneous interest	£1.50

MILITARY AIRCRAFT

Artist Drawn

Tuck R. & Sons In The Air	£4/6
Celesque Series	£4/6
Mack W.E.	£4
Salmon J.	£5

Real Photographic

Flight	£3
Aircraft Manufacturing Co. Series R/P	£8
Valentines	£5

Nulli Secundas, published by Tuck R.Sons, Embossed £15

Curtiss Army biplane, Published by Gale & Polden, £12

Airships

Nulli Secundus Pr.Photo c.1907	£6
Beta/Gamma	£12/£15
Zeppelins Close-up	£12
Combat sketches	£3/5

German WW2 £8

Aircraft

Royal Flying Corp 1912-18
Royal Naval Air Service 1914-18

Pilots/Machines	£10/12
Groups/Machines named Sqdn.	£15/20
Aces/Machines	£20
Portraits	£12/15

R.F.C. & R.N.A.S. amalgamated in 1918 to become the Royal Air Force.

1918-1939	£5
1939-1960	£3

Miscellaneous

Airfields/Hangers	£8
Bombers/Fighters	£3
Flying Boats	£5
Gliders	£3

BAC/SUD-AVIATION CONCORDE.

The maiden flight of Concorde prototype 002. The Concorde supersonic airliner is exp
enter service in 1973 and will carry up to 144 passengers at speeds of around 1400 mph.

*BAC/SUD-Concorde, Maiden
flight of the prototype 002 £4*

*WW1
British
Bomber £6*

A GIANT BRITISH AEROPLANE.
Ready to start out on a Bombing Expedition

SPACE

It is now more than 40 years since the first astronauts walked on the Moon and the postcards produced at the time to celebrate this momentus occasion. Prior to this there were cards produced, mainly in Russia and America to illustrate the race to be first to the moon.
These cards are now interesting collectors worldwide and sell well at fairs and on the internet

Gemini two-man spacecraft shown in comparison to the Mercury capsule.

*Crew of
Discovery, £5*

*U.S.
Airforce,
The
Bomarc
Guided
missile,
£3*

Lift off for Columbia, april 12th 1981 £3

75

CHILDREN

One of the most popular themes for the early publishers of picture postcards, reflecting the tastes of our Edwardian forbears. Cards of Children and related subjects were published by the thousand. Perhaps the best known series is the `Queen's Dolls House', published by Tuck, while many of the early chromo-litho art studies, in their design and execution represent some of the most beautiful cards ever printed.

Market Report

Children haven't been wanted for some time but there are signs of a pick up in demand for the better artist drawn types. Collectors are still being very choosy at the moment.

CHILDREN

Angels

Art studies	£3
Photographic	£2

Babies £1
Perambulators £5

Fairies

Art Studies	£6-£15

Named artists can command a considerable premium

Photographic £3

Fairies £10

Nursery Rhymes

Art Studies	£4
R. Caldecott	£1.50

Named artists can command a considerable premium

Chromo-Litho studies

These range from quite ordinary types to spectacular cards, again with named artists at a premium. (see Artists Section)

Photographic Studies	£1-£3

Tuck R. & Sons

Fairy Tales/Art Series 3472	£25
Ping Pong in Fairyland/	
Art Series 1156	£35

Frederick Warne & Co.

Caldecott R./8 sets of 6/	
Nursery Rhymes	£1.50

DOLLS

Close-up photos	£6
Early Art cards	£8
Greetings type	£2

Mirror Grange

Tuck R. & Sons	£3

Queen's Dolls House

Tuck R. & Sons/Set 48

Price per card	£1
Complete Set	£60
Wembley Exhibition	£3

Titania's Palace

Tuck R. & Sons/

Two sets of 8 cards	£3
Gale & Polden	£2

TOYS

Bramber Museum	£1.50
Diabolo sketches	£5
Golliwogs	£15+
Close-up photos	£6
Greetings type	£2

Teddy Bears

Art Studies	£10
Photographic	£8
Pullouts	£15
Roosevelt Cartoons	£30

IT'S YOUR JOLLY OLE SMILE
WOT I LIKES.

Mabel Lucy Attwell with camera £6

GREETINGS
FROM

I WISH YOU
WERE DOWN HERE
WITH ME.

Unsigned Embossed, fine printing, worth £8

This little lad all dressed in blue,
Brings my Birthday wish to you.

A Greeting
for your
Birthday

M.G.Hayes, Birthday series 3421 £15

GOD JUL

NERMAN

Nerman, Children, Published by KC Kort £10

CINEMA

Not a subject much in evidence during the hey-day of the picture postcard, the majority of Film Stars collected today date from the 1920-1939 period. While other collectors look for individual Stars from the 40s to the 60s, which are also very popular,

Market Report
There seems to be demand at either end of the spectrum, with interest in some of the silent era stars and the late 1950's / 1960's era. The golden age of hollywood has left us with an abundance of cards from the 1930's and 1940's which have to be cheap to sell.

FILM STARS

This is a select list of names, whom because of scarcity or demand, are currently fetching prices in excess of Catalogue valuation.

Abbott and Costello	£15
Astaire, Fred	£4
Ball, Lucille	£6
Bergman, Ingrid	£9
Bogart, Humphrey	£6
Brando, Marlon	£12
Brooks, Louise	£30
Cagney, James	£5
Chaplin, Charlie	£7
Comic sketches	£6
Red Letter Stills	£3
Cole, Nat King	£12
Doris Day	£4
Davis, Bette	£9
Dean, James	£12
Dietrich, Marlene	£8
Dors, Diana	£10
Durante, Jimmy	£8
Fields, W.C.	£8
Flynn, Errol	£6
Formby, George	£8
Gable, Clark	£4
Garbo, Greta	£4
Garland, Judy	£9
Betty Grable	£7.50
Harlow, Jean	£7.50
Hepburn, Audrey	£15
Holliday, Judy	£8
Howerd, Frankie	£8
Jolson, Al	£8
Keaton, Buster	£6
Kelly, Grace	£6
Lamour, Dorothy	£8
Lanza, Mario	£8
Laurel & Hardy	£25
Leigh, Vivien	£10
Lloyd, Harold	£5
Lombard, Carole	£6
Loren, Sophia	£8
Mansfield, Jayne	£6
Marx Bros.	£15
Monroe, Marilyn	£25

Presley, Elvis	£15
Paul Robeson	£15
Robinson, Edward G.	£7.50
Rogers Ginger	£6
Temple, Shirley	£4
Valentino, Rudolph	£4
Wayne, John	£7
Welles, Orson	£8
West, Mae	£9.50
Wisdom, Norman	£6

Marlon Brando £12

Series

Dave and Dusty	£3
Pictures Portrait Gallery	£2
Cinema Chat	£2
Picturegoer/1921-1939	£3
/1940-1962	£5

The Picturegoer Series ran to 6600 cards, published from 1921 to c.1962.

Film Sets/Stills

Pre-1939   £4
1940 onwards   £6

Picturegoer and other firms also produced six-card sets of scenes from individual films. Prices for the most part follow those of the respective Stars.

Miscellaneous Publishers

Pre-1939   £2
1940 onwards   £4
Continental Stars   £2
Coral-Lee 1980   £1

JAMES DEAN, SAL MINEO AND NATALIE WOOD in "Rebel without a cause".

Above: James Dean in 'Rebel without a cause' R/P £12

With all Film Star postcards, the value is determined by the name of the artist. Cards of the 1940's,1950's and some from the 60's are in most demand, and a price of £4 would be realistic for the majority of artists from this period. For cards of the 1920's and 1930's, a corresponding figure would be £2. But there are exceptions as given in our select list, and including certain other names of significance, or with a cult following. As a rule of thumb, the well-known Star is worth more than the unknown.

Please note that plain back cards carry the same value as postcard backs.

ORSON WELLES

Orson Welles R/P £8

TOM KEENE

Cowboy Tom Keene £5

DORIS DAY, JAMES CAGNEY, CAMERON MITCHELL & HARRY BELLAVER in "Love me or leave me"

Above: Doris Day and Cagney R/P £5

Autographs / Ink Signed

Value is determined by the individual Star. Certain names are worth more than others. See pages 210 to 215 of this catalogue for a more in depth guide

CINEMA

MISCELLANEOUS

Bioscopes	£50
Cinemas Exterior close up	£35
Felix the Cat	£12

Cinema Organists

Dixon, Reginald	£5
Others	£4

Disney

Mickey Mouse/Picturegoer Series Nos.

452, 452a, 452b	£50
Foreign published/France/Holland	£10+
Other Disney issues	£8+

Dorothy Dandridge, 1960s £4

Cinema interior, Kilburn Empire £12

Disney, Mickey Mouse £12

Cinema Building, The Tower Solent £12

COMIC

The Comic postcard is a British institution. It is the yardstick by which most non-collectors judge our hobby! Everyone recognises the Comic card, with its bygone images of hen-pecked husbands, red-nosed drunks, saucy jokes, and embarrassed Vicars! It has been the subject of learned dissertations by authors as varied as George Orwell to Ronnie Barker. And yet, with the exception of a few named Artists or themes allied to other subjects, Comic cards are not as popular today as in former times.

Market Report
There is a booming trade in the slightly non-pc humour of the 1960's where McGills, Bamforths and the like are plentiful and cheap. Popular themes are political, gay interest or anything considered 'retro.'

SERIES

Bamforth & Co.

Pre 1918	£2
1918-1939	£2
1940 onwards	£1-£3

Tuck R & Sons

Write Away/Early Vignettes	£10
Write Away/Later Issues	£4

Fragments from France/
B. Bairnsfather

Numbers 1 - 48	£3
Numbers 49-54	£10

Sketches of Tommy's Life/
F. Mackain

Set 10/In Training	£3
Set 10/Up the Line	£3
Set 10/Out on Rest	£3
Set 10/At the Base	£3

Black Humour
Happy Little Coons/Tuck R. & Sons/

Oilettes/H.D. Sandford	£12
Other Black Humour	£6

Other Series

Write Off Series/Valentine	£5
Other 'Write-Away' Series	£5

"MY NEW BOY-FRIEND HAS GOT A LIMP"
"A LIMP WHAT ?"

Pedro, Saucy comic   £2

GENERAL

All unsigned cards of general interest may be grouped together into the periods listed below, with this suggested price structure.

Pre-1918	£1.50
1918-1939	£1
1940-1960	.50

Early/Chromo-Litho

Undivided back	£8
Divided Back	£3

Tuck Write-away series   £10

Phil May Comic £4

Taylor comic, £3

Donald McGill comic £6

Comic Boxing £6

TYPES

Listed below are suggested minimum prices, bearing in mind that certain Artist signed may be worth considerably more.

Angling	£3
Aviation	£3
Billiards/Snooker	£9
Blacks	£8

Cameras	£8
Card Games	£5
Cats	£2
Chess	£15
Cigarette Packets	£8
Corkscrews	£8
Cricket	£9
Crossword Puzzles	£5
Cycling	£3/£6
Dentistry	£10
Diabolo	£3
Dialect	£1
Drinking/Drinks etc.	£2
Erotic	£5
Fitness	£3
Fleas	£1.50
Football	£6

Military	
Pre-1914	£2
World War 1	£3
World War 2	£5-£20
Miscellaneous	£1.50

Military WW2 patriotic, £18

Golfing	£12
Got Any Cigarette Cards	£12
Gramophones	£5
Hatpins	£1.50
Hunting	£2
Jewish	£25
Lavatorial	£2
Limericks	£4
Maps	£3
Masonic	£20
Match Boxes	£6
Strikers	£15

Tom Browne, Cricket, £9

Motorcycling	£6
Motoring	£5
Obscene/Sexual	£3
Pawnbrokers	£5
Ping Pong	£20
Playing Cards	£5
Police	£4
Postal	£4
Postcards	£5
Postmen	£5
Prehistoric	£2
Pussyfoot	£3
Racing	£5
Railways	£2
Rinking	£3
Rugby football	£6
Scouts	£10
Smoking	£3
Suffragettes	£25
Telegrams	£3
Telephone	£3
Television	£4
Tennis	£8
Trams	£3
Wireless/Radio	£6
Irish	£3
Scottish	£3
Welsh	£3

EARLY CARDS

Postcards were first introduced by Austria in 1869, the first British postcard appearing on 1st October 1870. These were officially issued plain cards with a printed stamp and without a picture, and came to be known as postal stationery. The idea spread rapidly, and within a few years many countries were issuing these novel plain cards. On the Continent, shortly after their introduction, privately issued picture cards came into being, published in varying sizes, but it was not until 1st September 1894 that similar picture cards were permitted in Great Britain, being accepted by the Post Office one month later. These early British cards were known as Court Size. They were smaller and squarer in shape, being issued from 1894-1902, and led to an Intermediate Size from 1898-1902. Until 1902 all cards had to carry the message on the front and the address on the back, thus restricting the design on the card to that of a small picture, or `vignette', with the rest of the surface left free for writing. But on 1st January, 1902, after mounting pressure from commercial interests, Britain became the first country to divide the back, thus permitting both message and address on this side, leaving the front of the card free for a picture. This move saw the adoption of a universal Standard Size of 5.5 x 3.5in, and heralded the real beginning of picture postcards as a major collecting pastime. Other countries quickly followed, and the resultant explosion in picture postcard production world wide lasted until 1914, when the First World War brought an end to this `Golden Age'. This is the most complex heading in Postcards, impossible to catalogue in any depth, covering as it does many millions of undivided back cards published throughout the world from 1869-1907, by which latter date all countries had divided the back and adopted the Standard Size. The entries below will form a general guide to type and price for all Early Cards.

Market Report

This is a very popular subject amongst the older school of collectors and dealers. There is little quality material on the market to tempt them out of hibernation but anything outstanding will sell.

GREAT BRITAIN
POSTAL STATIONERY/PRE-1894
First Day of Issue Postcard

p.u. 1st October 1870	£400
Unused	£5

Penny Postage Jubilee/Red Card

p.u. May 1890/Guildhall	£50
Unused	£25

Penny Postage Jubilee/& Cover

p.u. July 1890/S. Kensington	£25+
Unused	£8

COURT SIZE/1894-1902
Gruss Aus type £25

Early Vignettes

Coloured	£25
Sepia/bw	£12

Postally Used

When the above cards are found postally used before 1897, this consideration of early usage would usually over-ride other factors. The prices given below may be taken as a general guide:

1896	£40
1895	£60
1894	£250
September 1894	£400

With all cards from 1895 onwards, certain rare types may fetch prices in excess of those given above.

INTERMEDIATE SIZE/1898-1902
Early Vignettes

Coloured	£10-15
Sepia/bw	£6

GB Views

Sepia/bw	£2

STANDARD SIZE/1899-1902
Gruss Aus type £20

Early Vignettes

Coloured	£12
Sepia/bw	£4

GB Views

Sepia/bw	£2

If postally used, a small premium may be added to the above prices. It will be seen that some over-lapping occurs in the periods of usage for these cards. This is because there are examples of different sizes known. With regard to the entry for GB Views, it may be added that the majority of these published before 1902, were mass produced common scenes of large cities, towns and holiday areas, and consequently of little interest to Topographical collectors.

Court size, posted 1899 £10

FOREIGN
POSTAL STATIONERY/PRE-1894
First Day of Issue Postcard

p.u. 1st Oct. 1869	£400
Unused	£12

GRUSS AUS/EARLY VIGNETTES

Anniversaries	£25
Festivals	£20
Heraldic	£12
Parades	£18
Souvenirs	£15

Early Vignettes

Coloured	£10
Sepia/bw	£2

For postally used cards a modest premium may be added, in keeping with the scale printed under `Gruss Aus/Topographical'.

Early Tuck £12

GRUSS AUS/TOPOGRAPHICAL

A difficult area to catalogue, for prices are governed by country of issue, design, condition, and if used date of postmark. The prices given below may be taken as a general indication of value for cards issued in Germany, Austria, Italy and Switzerland, although cards from the smaller towns here are usually worth more than those from large cities.

Fewer Gruss Aus cards were issued by other countries, and as a general rule, the more obscure the country, the higher the value of its cards, with those from places such as the German Colonies, Greece, Palestine, Singapore, and small islands forming the top price bracket of perhaps three times above our base rate.

Prices given apply to postally used cards, although this factor has little significance with later issues from 1896 onwards. Before this date, however, considerations of early usage leading to the field of postcard history may be felt to be of primary importance.

1869-1879	£60
1880-1884	£45
1885-1889	£40
1890-1895	£20
1896-1900+	£12

1896-1900 £12

Sepia/Black & White

From 1896 onwards the production of Gruss Aus (Greetings From) cards increased dramatically.

Those listed above are usually printed chromo-litho in solid colours from 1896 onwards, and in colour and shades of sepia before this date.

From 1896 we find a great many sepia and black & white cards bearing the legend `Gruss Aus', but these are not worth anything like the superb coloured examples. Their average price would be £2.

ETHNIC

Dealing with the races and peoples of the world, this subject was not much in evidence during the early days of collecting, this subject heading covers a fairly broad spectrum of topics mainly showing people in action throughout the world, similar to Social History in Britain. Although before photographic representation of the European Nude became permissible in France during the latter years of World War 1, the many similar studies of native girls offered a culturally acceptable, if hypocritical alternative.

Market Report
More appreciated on the continent than here. Unusual countries and primitive types are what is wanted. Ethnic nudes are still popular. Most of Asia and Oceania is a safe bet. Aborigines are in demand.

ETHNIC GLAMOUR
Cards in this section show girls either topless or semi-clothed.

Ceylon	£10
Ethiopia	£6
South Africa	£3
Sudan	£6
West Africa	£6
India	£10
Japan	£10

Egypt
Tuck R. & Sons/Oilette 7200/

Egypt - The Sphinx	£3
Miscellaneous types	£5

Senegal

Fortier/Dakar	£8

North Africa
The source of the great majority of Ethnic Glamour cards, depicting mainly Arab or Bedouin girls. The leading publisher was Lehnert & Landrock of Cairo and Tunis.

Lehnert & Landrock

Coloured/Numbered on front	£6
/Other series	£6
Sepia/Numbered on front	£3
Real Photographic	£6
Black & White	£3

Other Publishers

ELD/LL/ND/Geiser	£8
Real Photographic	£6
Miscellaneous types	£3

The following cards show girls fully clothed, but are different to the usual National Dress or Trades and Workers types in that they are specifically intended as glamour studies of beautiful girls in the context of their Ethnic background.

Europe	£1.50
Far East	£1.50
North Africa	£1.50

Cards may be found in both categories from certain other countries - Java, Indo China, Japan etc. Depending upon the image, such cards may be rated slightly higher than the above figures.

Ethnic, Senegal printed card £8

Aborigines £6

American Indians £8

MISCELLANEOUS

American Indians	£8
Cannibals	£12
Cowboys	£5
Fakirs/Snake Charmers	£4
Hats	£2
Opium Smokers	£5
Oxford University Robes	£1.50

Contemporary Fashion

c.1910 Family Portraits	£3

Curiosities

Houses/Models etc.	£2
Natural/Trees etc.	£2

Great Britain

Portraits of People/Groups	£2

Ireland

Irish Humour	£3
People/Costume/Life etc.	£3

Japan

Chromo-Litho vignettes	£12
Hand Painted/Black & Gold	£6
/Other types	£4
Art cards	£3
Art Reproductions/Hiroshige etc.	£1.50
Museum cards	£1
Geisha	£6
People/Costume/Life etc.	£1.50
Temples/Cherry Blossom etc.	£1

Masonic

Are You a Mason?/24 cards	
Millar & Lang	£20
Regalia/Miscellaneous	£8

National Dress

Misch & Stock/Stengel etc.	£1.50
Miscellaneous types	£1

Native Races

South American Indians	£5
Other Native Tribes	£5
Local Industries	£2
People/Costume/Life etc.	£1.50

Russia

Types of Russian Life	£12
People/Costume/Art	£4

Scotland

Types of Scottish Dress/Castle Series	£5
Scottish Humour	£2
Highland Washing scenes	£2
People/Costume/Life etc.	£1.50

Wales

Welsh Humour	£2
People/Costume/Life etc.	£2

See also 'Ethnic' listing under individual countries.

JEWISH POSTCARDS

The subjects of Jewish postcards ranged from New Year's greeting cards, Synagogues & Palestine, to those featuring specific Jewish themes like Jewish Holidays, famous Jewish people and Rabbis.

SYNAGOGUES

This is a very collectable subject. The synagogues of Germany, Austria and East Europe are very much in demand especially the ones that were destroyed during the Pogroms & Second World War. (£30 - £40)

Northern American & French Synagogues are more common and therefore less desirable.
(£8 - £15)

Rabbi £6

Early greeting with Jewish interest £15

NEW YEARS GREETING CARDS

Sending Jewish New Years cards has always been very popular. Most of the cards had no specific Jewish motive but the pictures were taken from different sources. Many of the images were staged, often featuring models that made multiple appearances in different settings but they faithfully represented realistic elements of daily life.

"Happy New Year" in Hebrew, English and Yiddish, and a short poem was often added. (£5 - £10)

PALESTINE

Most of the postcards of Palestine are topographical or historical. There are mainly cards of towns and street scenes. Some postcards mark special occasions like a visit of an important person etc.
(£5 - £10)

The New Years greeting cards that were published in Poland & Russia are rare and therefore more valuable. (£30 - £60)

Jerusalem, £3

New Years Card £8

EXHIBITIONS

A vast and complex field with many Exhibitions well able to support their own specialised Catalogue. All the events listed below had picture postcards issued, some of which were sold at retail outlets throughout the country, quite removed from the Exhibition itself. All one can do here is to list the main events, and give a suggested minimum price per card, bearing in mind that certain cards may be worth more if depicting Trade Stands, carrying Advertisements, or bearing an Artist's signature. This whole section needs to be re-done by an expert in the field

Market Report
This section is experiencing something of a revival. If you can plough your way through the common material, there is now strong demand for anything unusual, particularly from the 1908 Franco-British and 1924 Wembley Exhibitions.

GREAT BRITAIN

Scottish National Exhibition, 1908 £4

Royal Naval Exhibition/S.W.
Eddystone Lighthouse
p.u.1891/Violet postmark	£75
p.u. 1891/Blue postmark	£75

Gardening & Forestry Exhibition
Eddystone Lighthouse
p.u. 1893/Earls Court	£150
Unused	£75

Victorian Era 1897
Earls Court	£50

Women's Exhibition 1900
Earls Court/Dinka Village	£5

Glasgow 1901
Cassiers H.	£8
bw views	£4

Military 1901
Earls Court	£6

Cork 1902 £5

Wolverhampton 1902 £6

Highland & Jacobite 1903
Inverness	£5

International Fire 1903
Earls Court	£5

Scottish Home Industries 1903
Manchester	£5

Bradford 1904 £3

International Gas 1904
Earls Court	£5

Italian 1904
Earls Court	£3

Nottingham 1904
Fire scenes/General views	£3

Colonial 1905
Crystal Palace	£5

Imperial Austrian 1906
Earls Court	£1.50

Balkan States 1907
Earls Court	£3

Irish International 1907
Dublin	£3

South African Products 1907
Poster Advert Card	£12

Crystal Palace 1908 £5

Hungarian 1908 £2

Scottish National 1908
Edinburgh	£2-£4

Worlds Mining 1908
Olympia	£5

Franco-British 1908
Mucha	£150
Woven Silk	£60
Trade Stands	£8

Festival of Empire, Crystal Palace 1911, £4

89

Hagenbeck Circus/Stadium	£8	**Shakespeare's England 1912**		
Comic/Patriotic	£4	Earls Court	£1.50	
Views	£1.50			
Imperial International 1909		**Building Trades 1913**		
Trade Stands	£8	Olympia	£3	
Patriotic/Tartar Camp	£5	**Imperial Services 1913**		
Views	£1.50	Earls Court	£3	
C.M.S. Africa & The East 1909				
Islington	£3	**Liverpool 1913**	£3	
Golden West 1909		**Russian Village 1913**		
Earls Court	£3	Olympia	£3	
Japan-British 1910		**Anglo-American 1914**		
Trade Stands	£8	Band/Patriotic/Wild West	£5	
Comic/Patriotic	£3	White City/Views	£2	
Views	£2			
Coronation 1911		**Anglo-Spanish 1914**		
Trade Stands	£8	Earls Court	£3	
White City Views	£3			
Festival of Empire 1911		**Bristol International 1914**	£3	
Oxo/Patriotic	£8	**Newcastle upon Tyne 1929**	£3	
Crystal Palace/Views	£4			
Scottish National 1911		**Empire 1938**		
Glasgow	£2	Glasgow	£1.50	
		Festival of Britain 1951		
Jubilee International Stamp 1912		Signed Watercolours	£8	
Victoria S.W./Ideal Stamp	£10	Far Tottering & Oyster Creek Railway	£5	
Latin-British 1912		Views	£3	
White City	£1.50			

British Empire Exhibition, Wembley 1924, £3

90

Miscellaneous Exhibitions

Daily Mail/Flower Shows etc.	£2
Cards printed on Stands	£8

BRITISH EMPIRE 1924/25
Advertising Cards

Cope Bros/Poster Adverts	£60
Tuck R. & Sons by C.E. Flower/	
APOC/North British Rubber/	
Bryant & May/Sharp's etc.	£12
Anchor Line/HMV etc.	£12

Court & Pavilion cards

Australia/Bengal/Bombay etc.	£3
Falklands Court	£50

Exhibition views

Tuck R. & Sons/Coloured	£4
Fleetway/Sepia	£1.50
Other Publishers/RP & Coloured	£3
/Sepia	£1.50

Colonial views

Tuck R & Sons/RP	£3
/Coloured	£3

Overseas Exhibition £4

/Sepia	£2
Other Publishers/Sepia	£1.50
Queens Doll's House	
Tuck R. & Sons	£3

PAGEANTS U/K	**£2**

For full listings of UK and overseas Pageants see Picture postcard values 2003

OVERSEAS EXHIBITIONS

With hundreds of overseas Exhibitions held world-wide during the past century, it is neither realistic nor practical to attempt to list every single one, let alone give prices for all their cards. Many of these Exhibitions could support their own Catalogue! As for pricing, any attempt at this is dependent upon knowing exactly what was published, and this information is not yet in the public domain. As a general guide the following price structure may be of some help:

1881-1895	**£20/£40**
1896-1900	**£10/£20**
1901-1905	**£2/£12**
1906-1918	**£1/£5**
1919 onwards	**£1/£3**

Any pre-1907 card of Gruss Aus design would be worth at least £10, but other early bw or sepia cards such as those from Paris 1900 would be valued at around £1.50. It must be further pointed out that the unusual or spectacular card, such as a Poster Advert, from any Exhibition may be worth considerably more than its range given above while at the same time some Exhibitions may be more popular than others.

Paris 1933 £12

PAGEANTS/OVERSEAS

Quebec 1908	£2
Hudson-Fulton 1909	£5
Capetown 1910	£2
National Fetes	£3

EXPLORATION

The explorations and expeditions of the Edwardian Age were well covered by the picture postcards of the time, albeit in smaller production runs than the more popular themes. For this reason the cards which remain are difficult to find and consequently highly priced.

Market Report

A very popular subject which is much sought after but seldom found. Prices tend to be determined at auction as very little is discovered in dealers stocks.

Above: Tuck R. & Sons/Oilettes/Operati A. £8
Right: Arctic, Meissner & Buch series 1016, 1897, £25
Below; Captain Scott and his ship 'Terra Nova' £15

POLAR

All prices are for unused cards; beware modern reproductions.
Cards sent from expeditions carry a large premium.

ANTARCTIC

1897-99 de Gerlache (Belgium)

Set 12 pub. Nels each	£25
Return of expedition 1899	£40
Various cards	£30

1901 Drygalski (Germany)

Set 5 Artist drawn cards each	£125

1901-04 Nordenskjold (Sweden)

Set 10 'S.Y.Antarctic' exp. each	£60
Argentine rescue cards various	£50

1901-04 Scott
Set 4 Wrench Links of Empire

p.u. from ports of call each	£150
Set 24 Canterbury Times each	£45
Set 12 Weekly Press each	£80
Ship 'Discovery' various	£25

1903-05 Charcot (France)

Set 6 for subscribers (Tuck) p.u. each	£100
Launch of 'Francais'1903	£40
Set 20 Expedition cards each	£50
Various cards of ship 'Francais'	£30

1904 Scottish National Expedition

Set 12 pub W.Ritchie each	£50
Various pub. in Argentina	£40
Ship 'Scotia' various	£35

1907-09 Shackleton

Set 12 expedition views each	£20
With printed adverts	£30
Ship 'Nimrod' various photos	£25+
Shackleton various photos	£20

1908-10 Charcot (France)

Launch of 'Pourquoi-Pas?'	£40
Various ship cards pub ELD, ND	£30
Expedition cards	£50

1910-12 Amundsen (Norway)

Set 5 chromo-litho pub Mittet each	£20
Amundsen photo	£25

1910-13 Scott

Set 12 Ponting photos each	£25-£30
Memoriam cards Rotary / Batchelder	£15/30
Various NZ pub ship 'Terra Nova'	£50
Advertising cards Fry, Shell, etc	£60
Memorials to Scott, statues, cairns etc	£8
Expedition memorial cards, various	£25

Shackleton, £30

1914-17 Shackleton

Set 8 sepia expedition photos each	£20
With Spratts dog food advert each	£30
Ship 'Endurance' in port	£40
Various Return of Expedition cards	£50

1921-22 Shackleton –Rowett Expedition

'Quest' at Portsmouth	£70
Various departure, crew members etc	£50
Shackleton's grave 1929	£15

1928-30, 1933-35 Byrd (USA).)

Set 17sepia photos 1929,each p.u.1934	£20
Set dog teams pub Neill NZ 1928 each	£60
1933 Fair 'City of New York' ship	£5
Expedition dogs, various	£10

1954 Australia research expedition

Map card	£10
Set 5 photos pub Seven Seas each	£10

1955-58   Trans-Antarctic   Expedition

Set 7 b/w photos each	£10+

ARCTIC

1893 Nansen (Norway)

Composite Set 4/Price per Set	£400
On board the `Fram'	£40

93

Aus Nansen in Nacht und Eis/Set 12/
Meissner & Buch/Series 1016 £20

1897Andree (Sweden)
Hot Air Balloon
Set 25/Bergeret, Nancy £60
Portraits etc/1930 discovery £15

1899 'Princesse Alice'
Prince Albert of Monaco etc in
Spitzbergen / set 24 £20

1899 Abruzzi /Cagni (Italy)
On board the `Stella Polare' £50
Rome Conference 1901/
Subscription Cards £40
Various cards £35

1901 Otto Sverdrup
Various cards £40

1903-1905 Ziegler/`America'
Various cards £40

1903 Swedish South Polar Expedition
'SY Antarctic' Expedition views / set 12 £60
Argentine rescue pub La Nacion / 16 £40
Various Argentine rescue £50

1908 Robert Peary (USA)
N.Pole Gravure /Hampton's mag/ set 13 £12
Kawin & Co./Chicago/Set 50/bw photos £8
Taggart/Series of sepia photos £6
Tuck R. & Sons/Oilettes/Operati A. £8
Ullman North Pole Series 162/Wall B. £8
S.S. `Roosevelt'/Inset Peary portrait/

Set 3 Official/p.u. 12.9.09 £75
Peary & Cook/Comic sketches £5

1911 Filchner (Germany)
Views of 'Deutschland', various £50

Hot Air Balloon/`Princess Alice'
Set 24/Alfonso XIII & Prince of
Monaco etc. in Spitzberg £30

1925-26 North Pole flights in Airships/
Dirigibles by Amundsen, Bennett, Byrne,
Ellsworth, Nobile
Various cards £30

1936 J.B.Charcot (France)
Shipwreck   1936 £35
Funeral   1936 £60
1954 Australian Antarctic Bases
Pub. Seven   Seas stamps / set 5 £8
1957 Trans-Antarctic Expedition
bw photos / set 7 £8

EVEREST
1922 Expedition
Group photo/RP £15
1924 Expedition
p.u. from Rongbuk Base Camp £20
SAHARA
1921 Capt. Angus Buchanan
Set 12/Portraits & Events R/P £8

FERI · N'GASHI · THE · FAITHFUL · CAMEL
WHICH · BUCHANAN · RODE · THROUGHOUT
HIS · JOURNEY · ACROSS · THE · SAHARA
· 3,500 · MILES . . . IT · WAS · THE · ONLY ·
CAMEL · TO · COMPLETE · THE · WHOLE ·
JOURNEY

Sahara
Expedition
£8

GLAMOUR

One of the stalwarts of the Edwardian picture postcard industry as shown by the great numbers handed down to us. Glamour cards in one form or another are to be found in almost every original album, although the top of the range Artists and photographic Nudes are none too common. These were to be collected mainly in France, or by our troops during the First World War.

Market Report
Collectors of glamour postcards tend to be very discriminating these days. There is always demand for top quality material. Anything less than perfect needs to go in the bargain boxes!

ART STUDIES
Chromo-Litho

Meissner & Buch	£15
Other publishers	£10

Nudes/Semi-Nudes

Pin-up type	£6
French Salon/Coloured	£4
/Sepia/BW	£2
Classical Art	£1

Pretty Girls

Better cards/Pre-1914	£3
Miscellaneous	£1.50

USA Post-War Pin-Ups

Machine cards/Plain back	£5

BATHING BEAUTIES
Embossed/Artist drawn

Chromo-Litho	£10
Other types	£5

Photographic/Portraits

Miscellaneous	£3

Meissner & Buch early Glamour £15

PHOTOGRAPHIC
Nudes

Prices given both for Nudes and Lingerie apply equally to plain back cards as these formed the bulk of publishers' output during this period.

France c.1916/RP	£15
Germany/Italy etc.c.1916/RP	£12
c.1916/Coloured/Hand Tinted	£18
Printed/Bw & Sepia	£6
Stage Acts/The Seldoms	£8
Couples	£8
Between the Wars	£6
Post-War studies	£3
Body Stocking types	£4
Private photographs	£2
Modern reproductions	£1.50

Photographic nude   £12

SM Interest
Numbered RP series c.1920	£20
Bondage/Spanking etc.	£15

Lingerie Studies
	£10

Pretty Girls
Better cards/Pre-1914	£3
Miscellaneous	£1

MISCELLANEOUS
Pornographic/Postcard back
Art/Photographic	£18

Plain back cards have no commercial value otherthan curiosity appeal.

Lesbian interest
	£18

Erotica
Photographic	£18
Art	£6
Comic Sketches	£6

Bedroom Scenes
Art/Photographic	£4

Miss Europe Competition
RP studies of contestants	£3

Bathing Glamour £12

Art Nouveau Unsigned £20

GLAMOUR

Asti £6

German Romance, £7

Patriotic Glamour £6

Xavier Sager £15

97

GREETINGS

Greetings Cards in one form or another provided the bulk of the Edwardian publishers' output. Birthday and Christmas cards of all types were produced in their millions, while the better Embossed cards remain as superb examples of the printer's art. Coin and Stamp Cards were published in long series, although these have never been too popular in today's market. Other themes have been grouped together to make this heading.

Market Report
This category tends to suffer from an over supply of mundane material but which can hide hidden gems. Worth a rummage as prices are low for the quality of some of the cards here.

COIN CARDS
National Coinage

Embossed	£8
Printed	£5

Banknote Cards

Embossed	£8
Printed	£5

DATE CARDS
Turn of the Century/Postally used

Sent 31.12.99/Received 1.1.00	£30

Year Dates/Up to 1903

Embossed	£10
Printed	£3

Year Dates/1904 onwards

Embossed	£6
Printed	£4

Calendar Cards	£4

EMBOSSED

Grade A	£12
Grade B	£5
Grade C	£1

These are as difficult to describe as they are to illustrate! At the top of the range are the superb chromo-litho cards of ornate design, in the middle are the great bulk of nice Embossed, while below these come the common, run of the mill types.

FANTASY

Enlarged Objects	£4
Erotic	£12
Faces in Smoke etc.	£4
Fantasy Maps	£15
Multi-Babies	£3-6

Fantasy Heads

Coloured	£25
Black & White	£10

Faces in Mountains

Pub. Killinger	£12
Later issues	£4

Fantasy map, £15

Greetings £4

FATHER CHRISTMAS

Hold to Light type	£85
WWI Silk type	£25
Tuck Oilette	£8
Coloured	£6
Photo type	£3
Snowmen	£3

Early embossed

Red robes	£15
Other Coloured Robes	£16

Prices are for good full-length or full-face Santas. Small designs or those with Santa forming part of a larger picture are worth less.

LANGUAGE

Deaf and Dumb Alphabet	£5
Language of Fruit	£2
Language of Stamps	£2
Language of Vegetables	£2

Esperanto

Tuck R. & Sons/Oilette series	£8
Miscellaneous issues	£3/£5

Language of Flowers

Welch J & Sons	£1.50
Miscellaneous issues	£1.50

Date Card, £3

RECREATIONAL

Casinos	£1.50
Playing Cards	£8
Roulette Wheel Cards	£2

Romance

Cupid's Darts/Welch J. & Sons	£1.50
Proverbs/Welch J. & Sons	£1.50
Miscellaneous Comic Types	£1.50
Greetings/Sentimental/Lovers	£1

LARGE LETTER

Names of People	£2
Names of Places	£2
Numbers	£2

Cherubs

Tuck R. & Sons	£12
Other series Embossed	£8
Printed	£4

Initials

Colour embossed	£8
Coloured	£4
B/W & Sepia	£2

Christmas Greeting £2

SEASONAL GREETINGS

Christmas	£1-3
Decoration Day	£6
Easter	£1
Halloween	£8
Independence Day	£4
New Year	£1
Poisson d'Avril	£1
St. Patrick's Day	£3
Thanksgiving Day	£3
Valentine's Day	£5

These are prices representing the average card found in any section, but the spectacular item will fetch considerably more.

Birthday

Deckle-edge c.1930	.50
Miscellaneous	£1

Stamp Cards, Embossed, £8

STAMP CARDS

Embossed	£8
Printed	£5

Certain countries, e.g. Canada, realise a considerable premium.

MISCELLANEOUS

Champagne Bottles	£5
Davis Message Cards	£1.50
Fireworks	£6
Flowers	£1
Fruit	£1
Hands Across the Sea	£1.50
Moonlight	£1
Mottos/Sayings	£1
Rough Seas	£1
Swastikas/Greetings type	£1

Faith, Hope and Charity

Set 3	£5
Single cards	£1.50

Silhouettes

Camp Silhouette Series/ 25 cards/Photochrom Co.	£4
Cut-out types	£6
Printed types	£2

Smoking

Cigarette Card Comics	£20
Cigarettes/Pipes/Tobacco	£4

Miscellaneous Greetings

Better cards/Pre-1914	£3
General Types	£1

With the lower value Greetings cards, Christmas and Birthday etc., anything Embossed, or printed Chromo-Litho, or carrying an unusual design, would certainly be worth more.

Large Letter, £2

Seaside greeting embossed, £4

HERALDIC

Originally far more popular than they are now, Heraldic cards of all kinds were published in profusion by the Edwardians. Perhaps the sense of identity with a particular town or city was stronger then than it is now, certainly this would account for the enormous numbers of cards left to us.

Market Report
Not a popular subject these days. The topographic element will dictate sales if modestly priced. Early map cards are ready sellers though.

FULL OUT CRESTS

Faulkner C.W. & Co.	£3
Ja-Ja- Heraldic Series	
Stoddart & Co.	£2
School/University Arms	
Robert Peel Postcard Co	£1.50
Reliable Series	
W. Ritchie & Sons	£1.50
Multi-crest cards	£1
Special Crests	
Sports/Occupations	£1.50
Miscellaneous Publishers	
Better cards/Pre-1914	£2
General issues	£1

Ja-Ja heraldic series £2

CRESTS WITH VIEWS

B & R's Camera Series	
Brown & Rawcliffe	£1.50
Faulkner C.W. & Co.	
Cathedrals/Stately Homes	£1.50
Favourite Series	
W.E. Byers	£1
F.S.O. Heraldic Series	£2
Ja-Ja- Heraldic Series	
Stoddart & Co.	£3
Jarrold's Series	£1
Robert Peel Postcard Co.	£1.50
Reliable Series	
W. Ritchie & Sons	£1
Tuck R. & Sons	
Heraldic Series	£12
Heraldic View	£2

Valentine's Series	£1
Miscellaneous Publishers	£1

MISCELLANEOUS

Papal Series	
Ferloni L.	£5
FLAGS/NATIONAL ARMS	
Aristophot Flag Series	£1.50
E.F.A. Series	
Excelsior Fine Art	£1.50
Faulkner C.W. & Co.	
Early series	£6
Arms of the Nations	
Kohl/Tuck R. & Sons	£12
Flags of the Nations	
Valentine & Sons	£4
Miscellaneous Publishers	
Embossed/Chromo-Litho	£8
Printed/Coloured	£1.50

TARTANS

B.B.	
Tartan View Series	£1
Brown & Rawcliffe	
Arms, Views & Tartans	£1
B & R's Camera Series	£1
Cynicus Co.	£1
Johnston W. & A.K.	
Tartan & Arms Series	£3
Stoddart & Co./Ja-Ja	
Clan Tartan Heraldic Series	£3
Tuck R. & Sons	
Scottish Clans Series	£3
Valentine & Sons	
Tartan Series	£1.50
Valentine's Series	£1
Wildt & Kray	
Badge & Tartan	£2
Miscellaneous types	£1

MAP CARDS

Early Chromo /Embossed	£6/ £25
Mountain Charts	£1
Romantic/Comic types	£1
Walker John & Co.	
Geographical Series	£8

LITERARY/MUSIC

Judging from the diverse range and numbers remaining, cards of Literary and Musical interest would appear to have been quite popular in the pre-television days of our forebears. A good subject to collect, reflecting as it does, a wide spread of artistic endeavour.

Market Report
The literary world has little to say for itself and music has gone rather quiet, unless the musician in question has signed the card - but that's another story. See page 210

SKETCHES FROM SHAKESPEARE " AS YOU LIKE IT "

Sketches from Shakespeare, As you like it
Published by Hildesheimer £4

DICKENS

Cassell & Co./Barnard F.

Character Sketches from Dickens	£4

Chapman & Hall

Dickens Novels/Set 13	£6

Faulkner & Co.

Pickwick Series/244	£4

Hildesheimer/Manning E.F.

Dickens Characters	£4

Jones A.V.N./Reynolds F.

Dickens Characters	£5

Stewart & Woolf/Crowquill A.

Dickens Characters/3 sets	£4

Tuck R. & Sons

Early Numbered Series	£12
Dickens Postcard Series/Kyd	£12
Dombey and Son/ Set 6/Oilette 6050	£3
Nicholas Nickleby/ Set 6/Oilette 6052	£3
With Famous Authors & Painters	£4
In Dickens' Land/Oilettes	£2
Dickens Characters	£4

Valentine

Dickens Characters	£4

Portraits/Sites/Events £1.50

MISCELLANEOUS

Alice in Wonderland

Nixon K./Set 6/ Faulkner & Co./Series 1819	£12
Tenniel/Set 8/ Fuller & Richard	£12
Folkard C./Set 6/ A&C Black/Series 80	£12

Literary Personalities

Early Chromos	£8
Later Portraits	£1.50

Lorna Doone

Scenes from Lorna Doone/ Set 12/Photochrom Co.	£1.50
Characters from Lorna Doone/ Valentine	£1.50

Poetry

Patience Strong cards	£1
Verses/Miscellaneous	£1

Sherlock Holmes £12

SHAKESPEARE

Ackermann/Munich

Silhouettes/Set 12	£5

Faulkner & Co.

Shakespeare Series	£5

Hildesheimer/Carter S.

Sketches from Shakespeare	£4

Nister E.

Scenes from Shakespeare/ub	£8
Later series/Divided back	£2

Tuck R. & Sons

Early Numbered Series	£12
Hamlet/Set 12/Copping H.	£5
Merry Wives of Windsor/ Series 466-477	£5
In Shakespeare's Country/Oilettes	£2

Valentine

Characters from Shakespeare	£2

Portraits/Sites/Events £1

BANDS

Brass Bands	£6
Dance Bands	£10
Military Bands	£6
Pipe Bands	£5
Dagenham Girl Pipers	£3
Champion Bandsmen	£4
Band Leaders	£5

OPERA

Gilbert & Sullivan

Savoy Co.	£12
Other Publishers	£8

Breitkoff & Hartel/Set 60

Wagner Series	£12

Faulkner & Co./Series 1401

Wagners Operas/Set 12	£15

Meissner & Buch

Wagner series	£18

Ricordi

Chromo-litho ub/Japanese style	£18
Madame Butterfly	£18
Tosca	£18

Tuck R. & Sons

Wagner series	£18

Opera Houses	£5

Opera Singers

Butt Clara	£5
Caruso Enrico	£20
Chaliapin	£20
Melba Dame Nellie	£10
Patti Adeline	£10
Tetrazzini	£10
Other Singers	£6

POP STARS

Beatles	£7-£10
Others 1960's/70's	£3+
Modern	.50
Elvis	£9

The Beatles, £9

Pop singer Eartha Kitt   £6

SONG CARDS

BAMFORTH

Set 3	£4.50
Set 4	£6

Prices are for complete sets

Odd cards	£1.50

OTHER TYPES

Miscellaneous Types	£1

Tuck R. & Sons

Illustrated Songs Series	£1.50

MISCELLANEOUS

Bandstands	£5
Bells	£1.50
Bellringers	£8
Hymns	£1
Musical Instruments	£3
Advertised by musicians	£6
Musicians	£3
Orchestras	£6
Singers	£3

Composers

Art Studies	£3
Photographic	£4

Gramophones

Art/Photographic	£8
Comic types	£5

Jazz

Bands/Groups	£12
Instrumentalists/Singers	£12

Organs

Church	£2

MILITARY

The Military conflicts of history from the Boer War to the present day have always been covered by the picture postcard. In a variety of styles ranging from actual battle scenes to the personalities, patriotic and propaganda issues of the period, the postcard was not slow to reflect current tastes and national sentiment. The many issues relating to the First World War form the largest catalogue.

Market Report

There is an insatiable demand for fresh material, particularly the real photographic WW1 material which needs identifying for the family history lobby. Bairnsfather is increasingly popular as are tanks, transport, the Dardanelles campaign and many other areas of this huge subject.

For Political Cartoons in all sections please see POLITICAL classification.

SPANISH AMERICAN WAR 1898

Miscellaneous types	£25

BOER WAR 1899-1902

Jamestown Raid	£40
St. Helena/Camps etc.	£25
War Photographs	£15
Sites & Events/Historic	£5

City Press

C.I.V./bw Vignettes	£15

Collectors Publishing Co.

Personalities/Photographic	£15

Koumans P.J.

Personalities/Photographic	£15

Picture Postcard Co.

War Sketches/Caton Woodville etc.	£20
Personalities/Vignettes	£20

Tuck R. & Sons

Peace Card/Coloured Vignette	£25
Souvenir of 1900	£25
Empire Series/Art Sketches/bw	£18
Overprinted for Victories	£30

Other Publishers

Early Vignettes/Coloured	£18
Early Vignettes/bw	£15

BOXER REBELLION 1900-1901

The Boxer Rebellion was an uprising by members of the Chinese Society of Right and Harmonious Fists against foreign influence in areas such as trade, politics, religion and technology. The campaigns took place from November 1899 to 7 September 1901, during the final years of Manchu rule in China under the Qing Dynasty.
The members of the Society of Right and Harmonious Fists were simply called "Boxers" by the Westerners due to the martial arts and callisthenics they practised.

War Photographs	£30
Caricature	£40-45

Publishers include Eysler, Bruno Burger, Kunzli freres

Troops, ships and railways	£25

Publishers include Franz Scholz, E.Lee, Brun et cie (Expedition de Chine).
Notable artist Willy Stower (ships)

Villages,towns,forts etc	£15

publishers as below, Max Wolff.

RUSSO-JAPANESE WAR 1904-1905
Military Review 1906

With Kobe Handstamp	£10
With Tokyo Handstamp	£8
Without Handstamp	£6

Early Vignettes Black & White £15

Russo-Japanese War, The deliverance of Port Arthur, Unknown publisher £5

Japanese Official
Post Office 1904 issue	£8
Photo montage/Art Borders	£8
Communications Dept/Post War issue	£5

Peace Conference
Knight Bros./Multi-view	£8
Miscellaneous issues	£5

Russian Outrage on Hull Fleet
Real Photographic	£5
Valentines/Other Publishers	£3

Tuck R. & Sons
Real Photographic Series 5170	£8
Russo-Japanese Series 1330	£8
Russo Japanese War Photographs/	
Set 6/Silverette 6534	£8
The Russo-Japanese War/	
Set 6/Oilette 6484	£6

WarPhotographs/Sketches
Hildesheimer/War Series 5224	£6

Other Publishers £5

ITALIAN-TURKISH WAR 1911-1912
War Photographs
Traldi/Milan	£12
Miscellaneous issues	£8

CHINESE CIVIL WAR 1911-1917
War Photographs	£15
Art Studies	£10

BALKAN WARS 1912-1913
War Photographs	£12

WORLD WAR 1 1914-1918
FUND RAISING CARDS
Anglo-Russian Hospital Fund	£4
Asiles de Soldats Invalides Belges	£2
Belgian Relief Funds	£3
Bovril/Lord Roberts	£5
British Ambulance Committee	£3
British Committee of the	
French Red Cross	£3
British Gifts for Belgian Soldiers	£3
National Egg Fund	£5
National Fund for Welsh Troops	£2
National Institute for the Blind	£1.50
National Relief Fund	£3
Performer Tobacco Fund	£6
Red Cross	£4
War Bond Campaign/Set 12	£3
Y.M.C.A. Hut Fund	£4

National War Bond Tank
Trafalgar Square	£6
In G.B. locations	£18

War Bond Campaign Postcard
Trafalgar Square	£5
In G.B. locations	£15

Weekly Dispatch Tobacco Fund
`Arf a Mo' Kaiser/Thomas B.	£4

War Loan/Patriotic Designs
France	£5
Germany	£6
Italy	£5
Russia	£8

NAVAL ACTIONS
Bombardment of Britain 1914	£12

Scapa Flow
German Fleet/Sinking etc.	£9
Zeebrugge	
WW1 Actions/Interest	£1

OFFICIAL STATIONARY/ FIELD SERVICE CARDS
Great Britain	£2
France	£2
Germany	£3
Other Countries	£3

WW1 Cpl. Alfred Burt V.C.Hero £12

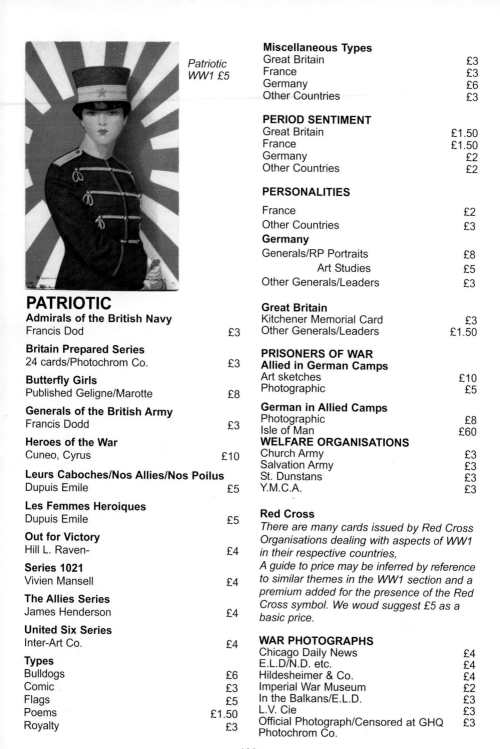

*Patriotic
WW1 £5*

Miscellaneous Types	
Great Britain	£3
France	£3
Germany	£6
Other Countries	£3

PERIOD SENTIMENT

Great Britain	£1.50
France	£1.50
Germany	£2
Other Countries	£2

PERSONALITIES

France	£2
Other Countries	£3
Germany	
Generals/RP Portraits	£8
Art Studies	£5
Other Generals/Leaders	£3

Great Britain	
Kitchener Memorial Card	£3
Other Generals/Leaders	£1.50

PRISONERS OF WAR
Allied in German Camps

Art sketches	£10
Photographic	£5

German in Allied Camps

Photographic	£8
Isle of Man	£60

WELFARE ORGANISATIONS

Church Army	£3
Salvation Army	£3
St. Dunstans	£3
Y.M.C.A.	£3

Red Cross

There are many cards issued by Red Cross Organisations dealing with aspects of WW1 in their respective countries,
A guide to price may be inferred by reference to similar themes in the WW1 section and a premium added for the presence of the Red Cross symbol. We woud suggest £5 as a basic price.

WAR PHOTOGRAPHS

Chicago Daily News	£4
E.L.D/N.D. etc.	£4
Hildesheimer & Co.	£4
Imperial War Museum	£2
In the Balkans/E.L.D.	£3
L.V. Cie	£3
Official Photograph/Censored at GHQ	£3
Photochrom Co.	

PATRIOTIC

Admirals of the British Navy

Francis Dod	£3

Britain Prepared Series

24 cards/Photochrom Co.	£3

Butterfly Girls

Published Geligne/Marotte	£8

Generals of the British Army

Francis Dodd	£3

Heroes of the War

Cuneo, Cyrus	£10

Leurs Caboches/Nos Allies/Nos Poilus

Dupuis Emile	£5

Les Femmes Heroiques

Dupuis Emile	£5

Out for Victory

Hill L. Raven-	£4

Series 1021

Vivien Mansell	£4

The Allies Series

James Henderson	£4

United Six Series

Inter-Art Co.	£4

Types

Bulldogs	£6
Comic	£3
Flags	£5
Poems	£1.50
Royalty	£3

Belgian Soldiers searching for spies £3

Bw series	£4
On Active Service/Set 48	£3
Sketch The	£4
Sphere The	£4
French Edition	£4
Sport & General Press Agency	£3
Tit-Bits	£3
War Photogravure Publications	£3
The War Series	£3
World War Series	£3
Yes or No	£3
Special Cards	£5

Daily Mail Battle Pictures

Numbers 1 - 96	£2
Numbers 97-144	£2.50
Numbers 145-160/Anzac Series	£6
Numbers 161-176	£4

This famous series was published in 22 sets of 8 cards each.

Real Photographic series	£6

Daily Mirror

Canadian Official Series/RP	£5
Coloured	£3
Sepia	£3

Newspaper Illustrations

	£3
Black & White series	£3
Coloured series	£3
Sepia series	£3
Shell damage Series	£1

Regent Publishing Co.

The War Series	£3

Tuck R. & Sons

At the Front	£4
The European War 1914	£3
Types of Allied Armies	£4

Miscellaneous

Great Britain	£3
France	£3
Germany	£5
Other Countries	£5

MISCELLANEOUS WORLD WAR 1

Allied Occupation/Germany 1919	£4
Armoured Cars	£6

Campaign Maps	£5
Cemeteries/Memorials	£1.50
Conscientious Objectors	£20
German proclamations issued in French towns	£4
Greetings Cards/Regimental	£6
Mesopotamia Campaign	£4
Palestine Campaign	£8
Recruiting Parades/Departures	£25
Refugees in G.B.	£25
Salonika Campaign	£3
Shell Damage/Foreign	£1
Tanks	£4

Christmas Cards

From POW Camps	£8
Miscellaneous	£3

Dardanelles Campaign

Gallipoli/Anzac Cove/Suvla Bay etc.	
Troops/Action	£12
RP Landscapes	£6

Dogs

Major Richardson's War Dogs	£8
Red Cross War Dogs	£8

Victory Parades

GB	£1.50
Paris 1919	£1.50

War Wounded

Brighton	£8
Miscellaneous	£3

Women on War Work

For the Cause/Tuck R. & Sons	£8
La Femme et La Guerre/Leroy	£8
Our Own Girls/Arthur Butchur	£8
Photographic scenes	£8-£20

There are many other photographic cards, particularly those issued by Germany, France and Belgium depicting different aspects of World War 1,

Women on War work, R/P £20

Join the Army and see the World
Good Pay——Good Prospects——A Fine Life

Full particulars from any Army Recruiting Office or any
Post Office

Recruitment poster advert, £20

RUSSIAN CIVIL WAR 1917-1921
Allied Expeditionary Forces	£15
Red Propaganda	£18
White Russian Propaganda	£20
Miscellaneous Issues	£10

GRAECO-TURKISH WAR 1919-1923
War Photographs
Smyrna	£15
Miscellaneous issues	£8

SPANISH CIVIL WAR 1936-1939
Gen. Franco	£15
Republican Propaganda	£20
War Photographs	£20
Military Personalities	£15

ITALIAN-ABYSSINIAN WAR 1938
War Photographs	£12
Coloured Cartoons	£20

WORLD WAR 2/1939-1945

OFFICIAL STATIONERY/FIELD SERVICE CARDS
Germany	£3
U.S.A.	£3
Other Countries	£2

PATRIOTIC

Great Britain	£8
France	£5
Germany	£12
Netherlands	£5
U.S.A.	£8

PERSONALITIES
France	£4
Germany	£10
U.S.A.	£4
Gen. Eisenhower	£5
Other Countries	£4
Great Britain	
Churchill	£4/£8
Gen. Montgomery	£5
Other Leaders	£3

WAR PHOTOGRAPHS/SKETCHES
Photochrom Co.
Britain Prepared	£3
Salmon	
Aviation sketches/A.F.D. Bannister	£5
Valentine	

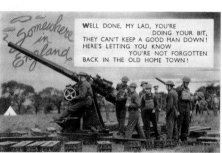

World War 2 Patriotic, £6

Real Photograph series/Aviation	£2
Aircraft Recognition silhouettes	£2

MISCELLANEOUS WORLD WAR 2
Prisoners of War	£10
Tanks/Guns/Vehicles	£5
V2 Rocket on display	£8
With The W.A.A.F./Set 24	£3
Sepia photos/Tuck R. & Sons	£20
Women on War Work	£12
Comic Sketches	
Bizeth/Sets of 6/Price per set	£36
Dutch Troops	£4
U.S.A.Troops	£4
Maneken-Pis	£3
Tuck R. & Sons	£4
Germany	
Erich Gutjahr Series	£8

This is an extensive numbered series of superb RP studies of the Germany Army in WW2.

Mit dem Werferkarren in die Feuerstellung

German WW2 Military £6

There are many photographic cards,
particularly those issued by Germany,
France and Belgium depicting different
aspects of World War 2, including Troops in
Action, At Rest, Anti-Aircraft emplacements,
Ammunition Transport, Convoys, Gun
Crews, Machine Gun Nests,Vehicles etc.
One may use a guide price of around £5 for
such cards, bearing in mind that some will
be worth more, some less

Germany/6x4 size

Generals/RP Portraits	£12
Patriotic Posters	£12
Hitler/Portraits	£12
Luftwaffe propaganda	£10

Peace Celebrations
Amsterdam Victory Parade 1945

6x4 size	£5
VE Day	£6
VJ Day	£6

Red Cross
As with WW1 there were many cards issued
by Red Cross Organisations in WW2
dealing with aspects of war in their
respective countries,A guide to price may
be inferred by reference to similar themes in
the WW2 section and a premium added for
the presence of the Red Cross symbol.
We would suggest £5 as a basic price.

Shell Damage

London Blitz	£4
Foreign	£1.50

USA

Troops/Action	£5
Pre-war Camp Life	£3

MILITARY ART

Gale & Polden

History & Traditions	£10
History & Traditions/Rates of Pay	£18
Regimental Badges	£6
Miscellaneous Coloured	£6
Knight Bros.	£3

Lavauzelle C./Paris

Early Vignettes	£8

Valentine

The Kings Army	£3

THE KING'S (SHROPSHIRE L.I.)

Helmet Plate,
1870

Cross Belt Slide,
1840

Regimental badge £6

WW2, Polish relief fund £8

Early Chromo, unsigned artwork VC winner
Advertising £12

Italian Regimental
Chromo-Litho	£12
Sepia/Black & White	£4

Miscellaneous Art/Coloured
Early Vignettes	£12
Later Issues	£3

Photographic Studies
Coloured	£3
Black & White	£1.50

Tuck R. & Sons
Oilette Series
3100 Cavalry on Active Service/ Harry Payne	£18
3105 Our Fighting Regiments/ The RoyalArtillery/Harry Payne	£12
3113 Comrades/ Harry Payne	£25
3159 The US Army on the Western Front /Harry Payne	£25
3160 Colonial Badges and their Wearers/ Harry Payne	£15
3163 Our Fighting Regiments/ 1st LifeGuards/Harry Payne	£15
3165 Our Fighting Regiments/ 1st Dragoon Guards/Harry Payne	£15
3204 Badges and their Wearers/ Harry Payne	£75
3205 Badges and their Wearers/ Harry Payne	£75
3546 Military in London/ Harry Payne	£5
3642 Scots Pipers/ Harry Payne	£8
6412 Military in London/ Harry Payne	£4
8491 Badges and their Wearers/ Harry Payne	£50
8625 The Scots Guards/ Harry Payne	£12
8635 The 21st Lancers/ Harry Payne	£12
8637 17th Lancers/ Harry Payne	£15

8731 Our Territorials/ Harry Payne	£12
8732 Wake up England/ Harry Payne	£15
8738 Types of the British Army	£30
8761 Defenders of the Empire/ Harry Payne	£12
8762 The Red Cross Series/ Harry Payne	£30
8763 The Royal Horse Artillery/ Harry Payne	£12
8770 Regimental Bands/ Harry Payne	£5
8807 16th Lancers/ Harry Payne	£15
8831 1st Royal Dragoons/ Harry Payne	£15
8835 1st Life Guards/ Harry Payne	£15
8848 11th Hussars/ Harry Payne	£15
8871 Badges and their Wearers/ Harry Payne	£15
8890 6th Dragoon Guards/ Harry Payne	£10
9081 Military in London II/ Harry Payne	£5
9132 Deeds of British Heroism	£8
9134 British Battles	£8
9139 Military Life & Military Tournaments/ Harry Payne	£5
9478 The British Army	£5
9527 Life at Aldershot/ Harry Payne	£15
9587 Military in London III/ Harry Payne	£5
9762 Scotch Pipers/ Harry Payne	£8
9883 Queens Own Cameron Highlanders/ Harry Payne	£12
9884 Gordon Highlanders/ Harry Payne	£12
9885 Seaforth Highlanders/ Harry Payne	£12
9934 For Home and Empire/ Harry Payne	£15
9937 Argyll and Sutherland Highlanders/ Harry Payne	£12
9980 Royal Scots Greys/ Harry Payne	£12
9993 Coldstream Guards/ Harry Payne	£12
9994 Black Watch/ Harry Payne	£12

Tuck R. & Sons
Military in London/Oilettes	£2
Unsigned Oilettes	£3

MISCELLANEOUS

Artillery	£2
Battlefields/Historic	£1.50
Battle of Waterloo	£1
Beefeaters	£1
Joan of Arc	£2
Napoleon	£3

Army Camps

Field Camps/Named	£8
Field Camps/Un-named	£3
Hut Camps/Named	£5
Hut Camps/Un-named	£2
Barracks	£5

British in India

Military Life/Sites etc.	£4

Italian Regimental

Menus/Patriotic/Seals etc.	£4
Chromo-Litho designs	£12

Life in the Army

Gale & Polden	£3
Star Series	£1.50
Miscellaneous photographs	£3

Medals

Present Day War Ribbons/Rees H.	£4
V.C. Winners/Various issues	£10
Daring Deeds	£3

Military Tattoos/Displays

Aldershot	£1.50
Royal Tournament	£1.50
Miscellaneous Events	£1.50

Uniforms/Dress

Mrs. Albert Broom series/Guardsmen	£8
Regimental photographs	£3
Identified	£3
Unidentified	£1.50

Unknown Warrior

Cenotaph Services/Parades	£2

There are many photographic cards depicting aspects of pre-war Military Life in different countries, including Troops on exercise, Parades, Training etc. One may use a guide price of around £3 for such cards, bearing in mind that some will be worth more, some less.

Harry Payne, Red Cross Series £30

Bamforth song cards, £1.50 per card

NAVAL

A vast and complex section where we will attempt to give some idea of the types of Warships in H. M.'s service.

Publishers produced large quantities of cards relating to capital ships where crews often numbered 1000-1200+. These are common and so priced. Other R/P's of named ships in exotic ports and harbours are of more interest and priced according to location.

Market Report:

A popular subject but the more common material is getting left behind. Exotic locations and ships with chequered histories help. Scapa Flow material has sold well recently.

Early Vignette, German Naval ship £15

HMS Ernest, Early Vignette £15

BATTLESHIPS/CRUISERS

Tuck R. & Sons	
Empire Series	£20
Oilette Series	£3/5
Artist drawn	£3/5

Foreign Types

Early Vignettes	£15
Visit of US Fleet to Melbourne	
1908 / Embossed / Inset Ship	£18
Japanese Official/Inset Ship	£10/15
Pre - 1939	£3/10
1939 Onwards	£3/5

LIFE IN THE NAVY

Gale & Polden	£2/4
Nelson Victory Cards	£2/5

Miscellaneous

Shotley Barracks/HMS Ganges	£4
Ships moored off-shore	£4
Other Barracks etc.	£4
Wooden Walls (Training Ships)	£4-10
Fleet Reviews/Displays	£3
Naval Engagements/Sketches	£6/£8
Personalities	£2
Sailor's Photographs etc.	£2
Graf Spee sinking set of 12	£6

HMS Hamoza £4

Battleships at Honolulu £5

The Imperial British Navy

Battleships	£4
Dreadnought Cruisers	£4
Battlecruisers	£3/5
Cruisers	£4
Aircraft Carriers	£5/8
Sea Plane Carriers	£6-10
Flotilla Leaders	£3/4
Destroyers	£3/4
Torpedo Boat Destroyers	£4
Submarines	£4/6
Sloops	£5/6
Mine Layers	£5
Mine Sweepers	£5

Small Craft & Auxiliaries

River Gunboats	£8+
Monitors	£6+
Patrol Boats	£5
Motor Torpedo Boats	£3/5
Depot Ships	£4/£6
Repair Ships	£5
Hospital Ships	£15/30
Surveying Ships	£5
Yachts.	£3/6
1939-1950 R/Ps	£2/5

Others Include :-

Drifters	£6
Ice Breakers	£7
Target Ships	£3
Troopships	£8-12
Tugs	£3

HMS Lion at Spithead £6

HMS Queen £4

HMS Medina £5

HMS King Edward V11, Gibraltar £6

HMS Enchantress £6

113

Battleship "Rodney"   R/P   £4

Flotilla Leader "Keith" - Sunk 1940 R/P   £6

Battlecruiser "Hood" R/P   £5

Destroyer "Ambuscade" R/P   £3

Cruiser "Gloucester"   R/P   £4

Submarine "E9"   R/P   £6

Aircraft Carrier "Hermes"   R/P   £6

Sloop "Dwarf"   R/P   £6

114

Minesweeper "Harebell" R/P £5

Depot Ship "Titania" R/P £6

Monitor and Destroyers R/P £8

Repair Ship "Assistance" R/P £4

Patrol boat "P.40" R/P £4

Hospital Ship "St.George" R/P £15

Motor Torpedo Boat R/P £4

Surveying Ship "Flinders" R/P £4

NOVELTY

Today, as in the past, a strong collecting area, where the original publishers vied with each other to produce the exotic and unusual cards which now make up this category. Novelty cards are those which do something, or have things attached to them, or which deviate in any way from the norm.

Market Report
Traditionally a popular introduction to the hobby, this section is regarded with something akin to horror by most dealers. Cards that squeak, levers that get damaged, glass eyed cats and dogs…. Bookmarks, stamp montages and pull out town views are steady sellers though.

APPLIQUED MATERIALS

Dried Flowers	£2
Feathered Birds	£10
Feathered Hats	£6
Glass Eyes	£5
Glitter Cards	£1.50
Jewellery	£3
Lace	£6
Matchbox Strikers	£12
Material	£2
Metal Models	£10
Mirror Cards	£2
Photo Inserts	£1.50
Real Hair	£10
Sand Pictures	£4
Seeds	£2

COMPOSITE SETS

Animals/Set 3/5	£30/£50
G.P. Government Tea/Set 6	£120
Jeanne d'Arc/Set 10/12	£75
Jesus Christ/Set 10/12	£75
Nansen/Set 4	£400
Napoleon/Set 10/12	£75
Samurai Warriors/Set 8/10/12	£96/£144

Albert Memorial/Set 15

F.G.O. Stuart	£60

Map of London/Set 6

Tuck R. & Sons/Series 9352	£75

HOLD TO LIGHT

Exhibitions	£15
Father Christmas	£85
Flames	£18
Gruss Aus type	£10
Greetings/Churches etc.	£6
G.B. Views/W.H. Berlin	£4
Large Letter/Date cards	£15
Better Designs	£15

MATERIALS

Aluminium	£3
Celluloid	£3
Leather	£3
Panel Cards	£1.50
Peat	£3
Rice Paper/Oolong Tea	£10
Wood	£3

MECHANICAL

Blow Up	£20
Heat-activated	£6
Invisible Picture	£6
Kaleidoscopes	£30
Lever Change	£8
Moveable Hats	£5
Paper Chains	£15
Perfumed	£4
Push-Out Models	£20
Reversible Bottle/Sand etc.	£8
Squeakers	£5
Venetian Blinds	£6
Wagging Tails	£3

Kaleidoscope £30

Pull Out Postman, £6

Gramophone Records
Ettlinger	£6
Tuck R. & Sons	£6
Other Publishers	£6

Jigsaw Puzzles
Tuck R. & Sons	£20
Other publishers	£12

Roller Blinds
Early type	£25
Later issues	£5

Rotating Wheels
Early type	£15-£25
Later issues	£3

Stand-up Models
Exhibition types	£75

Tuck Gramaphone record £6

PULL OUTS
Animals	£3
Artist/signed	£5
Beer Bottles	£5
Buses	£6
Cats	£5
Comic	£3
Dogs	£5
Father Xmas	£10
Fortune Telling	£6
Hop-Picking	£8
Irish Subjects	£4
Mail Vans	£5
Military	£6
Motor Cars	£6
Postmen	£6
Railway Tickets named	£6
Shamrocks	£3
Teddy Bears	£12
Town views/multi-view fronts	£3
Trams	£8
Welsh Ladies	£3

SIZES
Folded	£3
Giant	£5
Midget	£3
Panorama	£5

Book Marks
Art type	£3
Actors/Actresses	£2
Egyptian Scenes	£1.50
Other types	£2

TRANSPARENCIES
Angels/Greetings	£6
Continental subjects	£10
Exhibitions	£15
Father Christmas	£12
GB Views/Hartmann	£8
GB Views	£3
Meteor	£10
Puzzle Type	£5

MISCELLANEOUS
Bas Relief	£3
Puzzle Cards	£4
Stamp Montage	£6

Shapes
Circular/Leaf etc.	£6

Three Dimensional
Pre-1914/With eye-piece	£6
Modern/Nudes etc.	£1

POLITICAL

This section covers a wide collecting field, reflecting perhaps a greater awareness of current affairs at the time. This is a major collecting area, covering Wars, Political satire and Social events, Campaigns and Strikes, etc. For more on this subject see our Military Section.

Market Report
Sentiment seems to change on a regular basis. Irish political, anti- Kaiser and Hitler comic cards generally are popular. Prices for suffragette material continue to be extremely volatile.

Boer War Cartoon card £18

CARTOONS/WAR
BOER WAR 1899-1902
Antiquariat Bremen	£18
Bruno Burger	£18
Friedello	£18
Kunzli Freres/Thiele A	£25
Regel & Krug	£18
Ropke & Woortman	£18
Vlieger J.G.	£18
Zieher Ottmar/Thiele A	£20
Leaders/Personalities	£15

BOXER REBELLION 1900-1901
Bruno Burger	£25
Kunzli Freres	£25

RUSSO-JAPANESE WAR 1904-1905
Hildesheimer/Hardy D	£15
P.L. Paris/Muller E.	£15
M.M. Paris	£1

WORLD WAR I/1914-1918
Great Britain
The Hun/E. Sachetti/	
Set 6/Geo. Pulman & Sons.	£8
Davidson Bros./Ludovici A.	£5
Jarrold & Sons/Punch Cartoons	£3
Tuck R. & Sons/Aesop's Fables	
Set 6/Oilette 8484	£8
Miscellaneous Publishers	£4

France
Les Monstres des Cathedrales	£6
Miscellaneous Publishers	£4

Germany	£6
Italy	
Sculpture Montage types	£5
Miscellaneous Publishers	£5
Edith Cavell	
Corbella T.	£10
Mourning Cards	£6
Portraits	£3
Grave	£2
See also Silk Cards	
Other Types	
Human Butterflies/WWI Leaders	£10
Raemaekers, L	£4
OTHER CAMPAIGNS	
Alsace Lorraine	
Hansi	£15
Miscellaneous Cartoons	£5
Bulgaria 1903	£12

CARTOONS/SOCIAL
GREAT BRITAIN
Anti-Semitic	£20
National Insurance Acts	£4
Shops Act	£4
Worker's Compensation Acts	£5

Fiscal
Tuck R. & Sons/Game Birds	£8
Bradshaw P.V.	£8
Premier Series-The Fiscal policy	£8

THE FISCAL PROBLEM, *(Illustrated)*
The Wrench Series No. 10819. "RETALIATION".

Comic card to satirize the Fiscal policy £6

118

HEXHAM DIVISION ELECTION, 1906.

VOTE FOR CLAYTON,
THE MAN FOR US.

Printed and Published by Hudson and Son, Livery Street, Birmingham.

Vote for Clayton! Canvassing cards £8

Masonic
Are You a Mason?
24 cards/Millar & Lang £15

Tariff Reform
Free Trade/Family in Kitchen £1
Other Types £8

Other types
Westminster Cartoon Series £6
Davidson Bros/Ludovici A. £5
Faulkner & Co./Moreland A. £6
Morning Leader Series £6
Walker J. & Co./Furniss H. £6
Wrench E./Punch Cartoons 1901 £8
Miscellaneous Publishers £5

FRANCE
Anti-Royalty/KE VII Debauchery £10
Russia/Czar Nicholas etc. £15

Orens D./le Burin Satirique
& other Limited Edition Series £15

ITALY
Fascist Cartoons £12
Mussolini/Portraits £10
/Hanging £8

Dreyfus cartoon, £8

DREYFUS AFFAIR
Miscellaneous issues £8
ELECTIONS
Candidates £8
Canvassing Cards £8
Poll Declarations £10

IRISH HOME RULE
ULSTER CAMPAIGN
Sir Edward Carson/Portraits £15
Meetings/U.V.F. £25
Political Cartoons £15/ £25

EIRE CAMPAIGN
Easter Rising 1916 £15
Gun Running £75
Leaders £35

Mr. Bonar Law, Hon. Walter Long, Sir Edward Carson, and Lord Londonderry watching the march past of 100,000 Irish Unionists, Belfast, April 9th, 1912.
WALTON, PUBLISHER.

Irish political rally, £25

Irish Rebellion, May, 1916.
Sackville Street in Flames. A photograph taken by a "Daily Sketch" Photographer under fire.

Sinn Fein Rebellion, 1916 £15

POLITICAL EVENTS
Meetings/Treaties £6
Mourning Cards £6
Funerals £6

Visits
Czar Nicholas to France 1896 £25
Miscellaneous visits £6

119

WW2 Churchill Cartoon £15

WORLD WAR 2/1939-1945 (ALLIES

All my own work by Grimes	£4
Anti-Nazi (Hitler Photo type)	£15
Bamforth Comic series	£5
ITMA comic	£5
Our Modern Army Reg Carter	£8
Miscellaneous Cartoons	£4/8
U.S. Armed forces	£4
'What a war' by G.Wilkinson	£4

NATIONAL SOCIALIST PARTY

Nationalist Socialist Party	£15
Hitler portraits	£12-15
Other portraits	£10
Mosley period	£20

PERSONALITIES

Tuck R. & Sons/Empire Series	£20
Sir Winston Churchill	£6/15
Lloyd George	£5
Prime Ministers	£3/6
Cabinet Ministers	£3
Governor Generals	£3
M.P.'s Memorial Cards	£6
Foreign Personalities	£2 / £8
De Gaulle	£6
J.F.Kennedy	£8
Martin L King	£8

Faulkner C.W./Series 41

British Statesmen	£15

Great Britain

Early Vignettes	£15
Portraits/Art	£3
Portraits/Photographic	£2
House of Commons/Lords	£1.50

National Socialist party propaganda £15

Personalities, Lenin £8

WHO SPENDS THE TAXES?

'Look here - I'm going in here to spend my penny and your penny - I shall buy just what I like with them 'cause I'm a man, and you'll have to stay outside and take what I get you, 'cause you're only a woman.

Printed and Published by the Artists' Suffrage League, 259, King's Road, Chelsea.

Artist's Suffrage League cartoon £40

German card, anti-foreign car imports £25

SUFFRAGETTE CAMPAIGN

Events/Demonstrations	£85
Leaders/Portraits	£70
Publicity Cards	£70
Misc. comic Non cartoon	£20

Cartoons

Davey Geo/Suffragette Series	£30
Valentine & Sons	£30
Nat Union of Women's Suffrage Soc.	£40
Artist's Suffrage League	£40
Other Publishers	£30

Published by the International Class War Prisoners' Aid and shows the 12 defendants in the trial of Communist Party officials. £12

STRIKES/MARCHES/UNREST

Seathwaite Navvy Riot 1904	£30
Leicester March to London 1905	£25
Belfast Strike 1907	£30
Laxey Miner's Strike 1907	£50
Winchester Riots 1908	£30
South Wales Coal Strike 1910	£30
Liverpool Strike 1910/11	
Carbonara Co.	£20
W. & Co.	£20
For full details on this series please refer to PPV 2003	
Cardiff Strike 1911	£30+
Llanelly Strike/Riots 1911	£30+
Thirlwell Strike 1911	£50
Ilkeston Strike 1912	
Coal Picking Scenes	£75
Sydney Street Siege 1911	£8
Smethwick 1913	£50
Tonypandy Riots 1913	£35
General Strike 1926	£25
London Dock Strike	£30-£45
Worcester Railway Strike	£50
Demonstrations/Meetings	£20

RAILWAYS

As the dominant mode of transport in the Edwardian years, this subject was very well covered by the publishers of the time. The Railway Companies themselves led the way with a great number of sets and series extolling the virtue of travel on their own particular lines, and here the less common cards, or those from the smaller Companies, are highly sought after. As well as the correspondence cards listed here, many ordinary set cards were overprinted for correspondence or advertising use. These command a premium of no more than a couple of pounds.

Market report.

The lesser seen railway stations are still fetching eye watering prices at auction while rolling stock and miniature railways have been shunted into the sidings.

OFFICIAL CARDS

A term used to describe postcards issued/sold by railway companies to gain revenue and to promote all aspects of their business. Subjects depicted include Hotels, Ships and Buses.

PRE-1923 COMPANIES

BARRY
Paddle Steamers	£10
Barry Island/Coloured view	£30
Barry Docks/Correspondence	£40

BELFAST AND COUNTY DOWN
Slieve Donard Hotel/Jotter	£10
Hotels/bw	£12

BIDEFORD, WESTWARD HO AND APPLEDORE
Views/Trains	£25

CALEDONIAN
Engines/Rolling Stock
Sepia	£4
Coloured	£5

Hotels
General views	£5
Interiors/bw	£6
Interiors/Coloured	£8
Poster Adverts	£20

Views
Coloured/ Valentines	£4

Caledonian Railway engine £5

coloured/ other	£6
Black/White	£10
Tartan Border	£8
Clyde Steamers/Clyde views	£10
Vignette/Multi-view/Pic both sides	£15
Green or Brown artwork/1903	£30

Poster Adverts
Shipping/Coloured	£30
Other types	£75

CALEDONIAN AND LNW
West Coast Joint Stock/Coloured	£8
Sleeping Car/Reservation card	£40
Royal Mail Route	
Coloured	£15
Black/White	£15

CALLANDER & OBAN
Ballachulish Hotel	£10
Views/Booklet sepia	£15

CAMBRIAN
Views	£6
Holiday Advertising/Correspondence	£12
Maps	£22
Vignette/PicturePostcard Co.	£25

CAMPBELTOWN & MACRIHANISH
Advertising	£80

CENTRAL LONDON
Celesque Series	£8
Maps/Rolling Stock	£20
1911 Strike	£50
Poster Adverts	£40

Exhibitions
Pillar Box Pullout	£35
Blow Card	£75

CHESHIRE LINES
Views/Correspondence	£30

CORK BANDON & SOUTH COAST
Views/Oilettes	£4

CORK BLACKROCK & PASSAGE
Paddle Steamer `Audrey'	£40

CORRIS
Views
Corris Railway Series/Photographic	£8
/Printed	£12
As above but Georges	£5

DISTRICT RAILWAY
Vignettes
Court size/Pictorial Postcard Syndicate £40
Intermediate/Pictorial Postcard Company £35

DUBLIN & SOUTH EASTERN
Hotel/Jotter	£10
Views/Correspondence	£30

DUBLIN, WICKLOW & WEXFORD
Peacock Series/Correspondence	£35
Views/Undivided Back	£35

DUMBARTON & BALLOCH JOINT LINES
Views
Black/White	£10
Coloured	£12

EAST COAST ROUTE
Flying Scotsman/Hildesheimer	£4
Views/Rolling Stock/Stations	£12
Vignette/Write Away	£10

FESTINIOG
Views/Photochrom	£8
Views/Valentines	£10
Poster Adverts	£90

FRESHWATER YARMOUTH & NEWPORT
Vignette/Picture Postcard Co.	£40

FURNESS
Engines & Rolling Stock/Series 18-19	£6
G. Romney Art/Series 12-13	£24
Exhibitions	£45
Poster Adverts/Series 21	£90

Views
Furness Abbey/Series 14-15	£1.50
McCorquodale	£4
Tuck/Series 1-7	£3
Tuck/Series 8	£4
Furness Abbey Hotel/Series 16-17	£6
HHH Series	£15
Sankey/Tours through Lakeland	£25
Vignettes/McCorquodale	£40

Steamers
Lake Steamers/Series 9-11	£5
Barrow & Fleetwood Steamers/Ser. 20	£15

GLASGOW & SOUTH WESTERN
Poster Adverts	£75

Steamers
McCorquodale	£3
Other publishers	£10

Hotels
General views	£4
Multi-view	£8
Tuck/Chromo-litho	£10

Views
Oilettes	£5
Vignettes	£20

GREAT CENTRAL
Immingham Docks	£4
Hotels	£6
Engines/Rolling Stock	£18
Restaurant Car	£15
Poster Adverts	£65
Perforated Engine Card/	
Central Advertising Co.	£90

Shipping
Overprints on other company cards	£20
Printed	£14
Photographic	£16
Turner C.E.	£12
Steam Ship Department	£40
Tuck	£30

Views
Faulkner Series 545 & 546	£8
as / panel cards	£4
HHH Series	£20
Vignettes/Picture Postcard Co.	£30

GREAT EASTERN
Stations./Trains	£6
Hotels	£7
Underground Railway Maps of London	£6
Southwold Bus	£15
Poster Adverts	£100

Views
Crest on Picture/Oilettes	£3
Crest on Picture/bw	£4

Shipping
Black & White	£8
Coloured	£10
Black & White/Correspondence	£12

Correspondence
General types	£25
Jarrold	£35
Oilette type	£25

Vignettes
Greetings from Harwich	£12
Tuck cathedrals	£75

Great Eastern Railway engine £4

Cathedrals

Faulkner/Series 118	£60
Faulkner with crest	£75

GREAT NORTH OF SCOTLAND

Views/Porter	£25
Cruden Bay Golf Tournament	£80
/Named Players	£100

Hotels

Palace Hotel Series	£15
Multi-view	£25
Multi-view/Pictures both sides	£30

GREAT NORTHERN

Hotels	£6
Correspondence	£25
Panoramic/Skegness & Sheringham	£30
Poster Adverts	£90

Engines

Photochrom	£2
Locomotive Publishing Co.	£5

Views

Photochrom/Coloured	£3
Black & White	£30

Vignettes

London views/Picture Postcard Co.	£25
Coloured	£40
Intermediate/Picture Postcard Co.	£35

GREAT NORTHERN & CITY

Views/bw Poster style	£35
Map	£50

GREAT NORTHERN/IRELAND

Correspondence	£15
Views/Overprint on picture	£25
Hotels/Multi-view	£18
Milroy Bay Motor Bus	£40

GREAT NORTHERN PICCADILLY &BROMPTON

Railway scenes	£10
Map	£25

GREAT SOUTHERN/IRELAND

Hotels	£6

GREAT SOUTHERN & WESTERN/ IRELAND

Views/Oilettes	£4
Joint with MGW/Wembley 1924	£25
Parknasilla Hotel/Motor Bus/	
Stage Coach Tours	£15
Poster Adverts/Parknasilla/	£70

Hotels

Jotter	£6
Lawrence/Correspondence	£12
Hotels in the Kingdom of Kerry	£20

GREAT WESTERN

Docks Series	£10
Fishguard Harbour/Route	£8
Motor Bus/Slough	£12
Restaurant Car/En Route	£18
Maps/with GWR crest	£40

Engines

Series 6	£2
Others	£4

Shipping

Photographic	£5
Coloured	£12

Views

Coloured or Sepia	£4

Hotels

General types	£4
Vignette	£8

Correspondence

General	£20
Wyndhams	£18

Great Western engine £4

Poster Adverts

General types	£50
Series 3	£90

Vignettes

Intermediate/Picture Postcard Co.	£25
/London views	£30
Court Size/London views	£30

HAMPSTEAD TUBE

Views

Last Link	£6
Multi-view/Map on reverse	£12

HIGHLAND

Map/Correspondence	£75

Hotels

Inverness	£5
Others	£10

Views

Circular crest/bw	£12
Straight line inscription	£15
Highland Railway photos	£25
Early coloured/Red circular crest	£40

HULL & BARNSLEY
Scenes at Alexandra Dock etc.	£35
Views	£35
Train	£40

INVERGARRY & FORT AUGUSTUS
| Views/Highland Railway series | £30 |

ISLE OF WIGHT
| Vignettes/Picture Postcard Co. | £35 |

ISLE OF WIGHT CENTRAL
| Vignettes/Picture Postcard Co. | £35 |
| Views | £40 |

JOINT SOUTH WESTERN & BRIGHTON
| Vignettes/Picture Postcard Co. | £35 |

KENT & EAST SUSSEX
Engines/Correspondence	£8
Views/1-6	£7
Other Correspondence cards	£35

LANCASHIRE & YORKSHIRE
| Correspondence | £30 |
| Vignettes/Picture Postcard Co. | £25 |

Engines/Rolling Stock
| General issues | £3 |
| Overprinted French | £6 |

Views
1905 &1907 series	£3
New series	£4
Overprinted French/All series	£5

Shipping
1907 series	£4
New series	£6
Overprinted French/All series	£7
Liverpool and Drogheda Steamers	£35

LIVERPOOL OVERHEAD
| Dock views | £25 |

LONDON, BRIGHTON & SOUTH COAST
| Correspondence | £40 |
| Poster Adverts | £90 |

Views
| Waterlow/Series 1-6 | £4 |

Vignettes
| French vignettes/Red overprint | £15 |
| Picture Postcard Co. | £25 |

LONDON, CHATHAM & DOVER
Vignettes/Court Size
| Black/White | £25 |
| Coloured | £35 |

LONDON & NORTH WESTERN
McCorquodale
Engines/Rolling Stock	£1.50/£4
Views	£1.50
Hotels	£4
Shipping	£3
Buses/Lorries etc.	£10
/Horse drawn	£6
Exhibitions	£20
Poster Adverts	£100
Maps/Correspondence	£100

London & North Western Engine £3

Tuck
Coloured/Royal Trains etc.	£1
Engines/Rolling Stock	£2
Views	£3
Shipping	£4
Hotels	£4

St. Louis Exposition/Undivided back
Exhibits/Multi-view	£6
Tuck/bw	£10
Tuck/Coloured	£15

LONDON & SOUTH WESTERN
| Orphanage | £4 |
| View with crest/Correspondence | £40 |

Shipping
| Black/White | £6 |
| Coloured/Early | £18 |

Poster Adverts
| Southampton Hotel | £45 |
| Other Posters | £80 |

Vignettes
Pictorial Postcard Syndicate	£35
Intermediate/Picture Postcard Co.	£22
London views/Picture Postcard Co.	£22

LONDON UNDERGROUND ELECTRIC
Poster Adverts
W.H.S.	£40
London Nooks and Corners	£40
Other types	£35

Midland Railway £20

LONDONDERRY & LOUGH SWILLY
Map/Correspondence £60

LYNTON & BARNSTAPLE
Views/Stations/Trains £18

MARYPORT & CARLISLE
Map/Correspondence £90

MERSEY
Views/Stations/Lifts/Trains £12
Poster Advert £80

METROPOLITAN
Correspondence £12

MIdland Railway Loco £2

Maps £12
VIEWS
Sepia/1-30 £5
Black/White £15

METROPOLITAN DISTRICT
Engines/Rolling Stock £5

MIDLAND
Engines £2
Rolling Stock £8
Midland Express/St. Pancras £5
Ships £6
Carriages £10
Exhibitions £18
Maps £20
Heysham Electric Train £25

Views
Photochrom £4
Nearest Station/Coloured £12

Hotels
General types £4
Vignettes/Coloured £6
  /Travel & Entertainment £30
  /BW & Sepia £18
Midland Grand Hotel/Business Lunch
£90
Vignettes
Black/White £15

Midland Railway Crash £45

Coloured/Andrew Reid £20

Poster Adverts
General types £25
Series £75
MIDLAND & GREAT NORTHERN JOINT
Views/Correspondence £40
MIDLAND GREAT WESTERN
Hotels £6

North Eastern Railway, Engine £5

Wembley Exhibition/Trade Stand	£15

MIDLAND/NORTHERN COUNTIES COMMITTEE
Trains	£12
Views/Correspondence	£35

NEWPORT GODSHILL & ST.LAWRENCE
Vignette/Picture Postcard Co.	£35

NORTH BRITISH
Ships/Coloured	£6
Ships/BW with crest	£12
Scottish Exhibition/Poster overprint	£40

Hotels
General types	£3
Poster Adverts	£8

Views
NBR Series/Caledonia 129	£3
Black/White & Coloured £12	
With crest	£14
Photo/White or decorated border	£15

NORTH EASTERN
Hotels/ York & Newcastle	£2
Hotels/ Others	£5
Riverside Quay/Hull	£5
Newcastle Electric Trains	£6
Brussels Exhibition	£12
Steam Goods Lorry	£50

Views
Photo Panoramic/1-40	£25
/Maps below picture	£30

Poster Adverts
General types	£75
Industrial Poster Reproductions	£90

NORTH STAFFORDSHIRE
Correspondence	£15

Views
McCorquodale/W&K	£4
W&K and W&TG/White border	£7
Golf	£30
Glossy anon.	£15

PORTPATRICK & WIGTOWNSHIRE JOINT
Ships	£18
Views	£35

SNOWDON MOUNTAIN RAILWAY
General types	£4
Snowdon Series/1-90	£8
Maps	£40
Poster Adverts	£60

Court Cards
Advertising/Hotel & Railway	£65

SOMERSET & DORSET JOINT
Views/Correspondence	£60

SOUTH EASTERN AND CHATHAM
Views/McCorquodale	£3
Engines/Rolling Stock	£3
Stations/Trains	£4
Hotels	£6
Ships	£4
London-Paris/English or French	£12
Bologne views/Stevenard	£12
Exhibitions	£8
Views/Correspondence	£25
Maps	£22
Poster Adverts	£90

SOUTH EASTERN & CHATHAM & DOVER
Vignettes
London views/Picture Postcard Co. etc.	£20
Intermediate/Picture Postcard Co.	£25
Pictorial Postcard Syndicate	£35

STRATFORD-ON-AVON & MIDLAND JUNCTION
Poster Advert	£100

VALE OF RHEIDOL
Views/Advertising overprints	£15

WEST CLARE
Views	£25

WEST HIGHLAND
Views	£6

WESTON, CLEVEDON & PORTISHEAD LIGHT
Train	£35

WICK AND LYBSTER
Views/Highland Railway Series	£35

WIRRAL
Views/Correspondence	£60

Miniature Railway Southsea £5

Map/Correspondence	£80

POST - 1923 COMPANIES
GREAT WESTERN
Engines	£3
Views	£4
Hotels	£4
KGV/Folded locomotive card	£75
Poster Adverts	£60

LONDON MIDLAND & SCOTTISH
Engines	£3
Hotels	£4
Ships	£6
Camping Coaches	£12
Views/Holiday tickets	£12
Container services/Removals	£35
Poster Adverts	£30

LONDON & NORTH EASTERN
Engines/Trains	£4
Hotels	£4
Ships	£8
Views	£8
Camping Coaches	£10
Paddle Steamers	£6
Poster Adverts	£90

Northern Belle Cruise Train
Unused	£25
Used on Train with Cachet	£75

SOUTHERN
Engines/Trains	£3
Ships	£5
Poster Adverts/LBSCR	£90

Views
Coloured/L. Richmond	£25
Correspondence	£35

POST-1947/BRITISH RAILWAYS
Hotels	£3
Ships	£3
Trains	£3

Gleneagles/Turnberry Golf Courses	£10
Seaspeed/Hovercraft	£1.50
Birmingham/New St. Station	£4
Correspondence	£4
Kyle of Lochalsh Station	£5
Poster Adverts	£15

NON-OFFICIAL CARDS
ACCIDENTS
Cudworth	£6
Grantham 1906	£4
Shrewsbury 1907	£6
Salisbury 1906	£6
Witham1905	£4
W. Gothard/In Memoriam type	£15/£75
Miscellaneous	£15+

OVERSEAS RAILWAYS
Engines	£3
Rolling Stock	£3
Stations	£1.50+
Views	£3
Official Cards/Crest or Title	£4
Japanese Official	£5

FRENCH POSTERS/OFFICIAL ISSUES
Orleans post-1920	£8
Artist signed	£12
Chemins de Fer de l'Quest	£8
Chromo-litho/Undivided back	£25

FUNICULAR & CLIFF RAILWAYS/LIFTS
Lynton-Lynmouth	£2
Other UK	£5
Overseas	£3

LOCOMOTIVES
Oilettes	£3
OJ Morris	£3
E.Pouteau	£4
Locomotive PublishingCo./ F.Moore	£2.50
Real Photographic	£2
France/F. Fleury	£3
Other Artist Drawn cards	£2.50

MINIATURE RAILWAYS
Ravenglass & Eskdale	£5
Romney, Hythe & Dymchurch	£3
Volk's Electric Railway	£3
Other Railways	£7

MISCELLANEOUS
Animated Scenes	£10
Bridges/Tunnels/Viaducts	£4
Level Crossings	£20

Notting Hill Gate, Tube station £25

Locomotive Works	£12	Others	£6
Locomotive Sheds	£6		
Motor buses/ road vehicles	£20		
Railway Staff	£10		
Signal Boxes	£15		
Trains on the Line	£3		
Hospital trains	£3		

RAILWAY STATIONS

Large City Stations

Interior	£8-£15
Exterior	£4-8

Others

Interior Real Photo	£40+
Interior Printed	£25-£35
Exterior Real Photo	£20-£40

Locomotive Publishing Co.

Vignettes/Coloured	£30
Vignettes/Monochrome	£25

UNDERGROUND RAILWAYS

London Transport	£10
Interior Real Photo	£20
Interior Printed	£18
Exterior	£10-30
Foreign/U. Bahnes/Metros	£6-12

MOUNTAIN RAILWAYS

Snowdon/Non-Official	£1.50
Overseas	£2

NARROW GAUGE

Vale of Rheidol	£3

Willesden Green Station £25

Underground Station Interior   £20

ROAD TRANSPORT

The majority of these cards were the work of the town or village photographer and produced for the local topographical market. Consequently they were never issued in any great number, which is why they are so highly rated today. There is an insatiable demand for unusual photographic studies, particularly where there is an added topographical element.

It is pointed out that for all relevant entries e.g. Buses, Lorries, Traction Engines, Trams etc. the stated prices are for cards, either RP or Printed, fully identified and showing a 'Close-up at a named location' with real photographic cards being the most desirable. Unlocated cards and middle or far-distance views would be priced accordingly.

Real Photo Motor Bus. Prices are governed by location and rarity This one could sell for £45

BUSES

Steam	£40
Horse-drawn	
Real Photographic (close up)	£30/£50
Printed	£15
London horse-drawn/Coloured	£10
Motor	
Real Photographic	£40-£60
Printed	£20
Charabancs	
Whole Vehicle	£8
Part Vehicle	£3
Coaches/Single-deck	£12/£20

Trolleybuses	
Pre-1939	£25
1940 onwards	£12

There are in circulation many privately produced, postcard-size, plain back photographs of Buses and Trams. Most of these have been printed in quantity from an existing negative and consequently have only a nominal value.

LORRIES

Petrol Tankers	£15-£30
Vans	£25
Coachbuilders' advertising cards/	
RP studies of Lorries/Removal Vans	£6-£15
Steam	
Commercial	£40
Military	£25
Motor	
Lorry Fleets/Groups/RP	£50
Commercial	£30
Military	£25

Real Photo Horse drawn brewers cart £35

130

Advert Cards

Poster Type	£35
Other Adverts	£12
Post 1960	£6-8

Where applicable, prices are for trade vehicles sign-written with company name and location.

Advert for Austin Healey £6

1930s Haulage Lorry, R/P £15

Morris commercial vehicle advert £8

MOTOR CYCLES

Close-up photo	£25
Photo other	£8-£15
Printed	£20

Advert Cards

Poster Type (Colour)	£35
Other Adverts	£12

MOTOR RACING
MOTOR CYCLE RACING
SEE SPORT PAGES 158-163

TRACTION ENGINES

Showmans	£50
Commercial	£30
Agricultural	£30
Military	£20
Steam Rollers	£30
Repair Gangs	£25
Accidents	£50

There are in circulation many privately produced, postcard-size, plain back photographs of Fairground and Showman's engines.
Most of these have been printed in quantity from an existing negative and consequently have a nominal value of maybe £5

Tram in the middle distance, this card is printed hence only £15

Motor cycle and side car £15

131

MOTOR CARS

Pre-1918	£12
1918-1939	£8
1940 onwards	£5
Garages	£30
Exhibitions/GB and Foreign	£6
Factories and Works/Interiors	£12
Celebrities of the Motoring World/	
Set 6/Tuck Oilette 9017	£6

Advert cards

Poster Type	£35
Other Adverts/Pre-1939	£15
/1940 onwards	£5

TRAMS

Steam Trams	£35
Electric Trams	£35
Horse-drawn Trams	£35
Track-laying/Removal	£35-£50
Trials	£30
Opening Ceremonies	£35
First Tram	£35
Last Tram	£20
Commemorative Cards	£25
In Memoriam Cards	£15
Tram Graveyards Early	£35
Decorated Cars	£6
Depots	£35
Works Vehicles	£30
Douglas S.E. Tramway	£6

Advert for Private Omnibus £30

First Tram, Real Photo £35

OTHER TRANSPORT

Ambulances

Horse-drawn	£35
Motor	£20

Royal Mail Vans £35

Fire Engines

Hand Drawn Real Photo	£40
Horse Drawn Real Photo	£40
Motor Real Photo	£40
Steam Real Photo	£50

*Real Photo
Steam Fire
Engine £50*

ROYALTY

I think the British Royal Family, and the many European dynasties at the turn of the century, must have been looked upon as a commercial goldmine by the Edwardian publishers. The vast numbers of cards handed down to us bears adequate testimony to their popularity at the time, when all types of Royal personages and Events both British and Foreign were subject to volume output by the picture postcard industry. I suppose the same is true today, as interest in this field has continued unabated through the years. And yet, it is perhaps fair to say that the wide public interest in Royalty and their doings, is not reflected in current price levels for historical picture postcards, for while the more unusual Portraits and Events will always sell, as will the many superb chromo-litho foreign commemorative issues, the bulk of the catalogue consisting of the more common GB types has always proved difficult.

Market Report
Standard British Royalty is a little out of favour. Later periods seem to be gaining support. In the foreign sections Russia still provides the trump cards but Albania and Thailand are worth looking out for.

GREAT BRITAIN
QUEEN VICTORIA
Diamond Jubilee 1897

p.u. 1897	£125
Unused	£65
Mourning Cards 1901	£15
Portraits	£8

KING EDWARD VII
Royal Tour 1901/`Ophir'
Wrench/Links of Empire/Set 20

p.u. from Ports of Call	£30
Unposted	£15

Royal Tour 1901 / 'Ophir'
Tuck R. & Sons/Empire Series 1649

p.u. from Ports of Call	£30
Unposted	£15

Coronation 1902
Tuck R. & Sons/Coronation Series/

Embossed	£10
Stewart & Woolf/Set 10	£10
H.Cassiers/London View Series	£8
Other Souvenir Cards	£6
Coronation Souvenir/bw	£4
Coronation Procession	£2

Visits to Paris 1903

Tuck R. & Sons/Set 10	£6
Voisey Chas./Set 15	£8

Death 1910

Mourning Cards	£2
Funeral Procession	£1

Visits

GB	£12
Foreign	£8
Portraits	£1.50

KING GEORGE V
Coronation 1911

Souvenir Cards	£3
Coronation Procession	£1
Delhi Durbar 1911	£3

Silver Jubilee 1935

Souvenir Cards	£3
Procession	£1

Death 1936

Mourning Cards	£3
Funeral Procession	£1.50

Visits

GB	£12
Foreign	£6
Portraits	£1

KING EDWARD VIII

Investiture as Prince of Wales 1911	£3
Coronation Souvenir	£6

H.M. KING EDWARD VIII.

King Edward VIII £6

Four generations of British Royalty £10

Silver Wedding 1972	£1
Silver Jubilee 1977	£1
Visits/Pre-1970	
GB	£6
Foreign	£4
Portraits	£1/£4

MISCELLANEOUS EVENTS

Coronation Bonfires	£20
Proclamations	£10
Royal Gatherings	£2
Royal Weddings	£3

N.B. Portraits include family groups. Less photographed members of the Royal Family, e.g. Prince John, together with other examples of minor Royalty, would be worth around £1.50+.

SERIES
Kings & Queens of England
Tuck R. & Sons/Set 42

Price per card	£12
King Insurance Co.	£6
Faulkners Series	£8

Wedding Souvenir	£35
With Mrs Simpson	£40
Visits	
GB	£20
Foreign	£15
Portraits	£2

KING GEORGE VI
Coronation 1937

Souvenir Cards	£4
Coronation Procession	£2
Visit to France 1938	£10
Victory Celebrations 1945	£5
Mourning Cards 1952	£10
Visits	
GB	£12
Foreign	£8
Portraits	£1.50

QUEEN ELIZABETH II
Marriage 1947

Souvenir Cards	£5
Betrothal Souvenir Cards	£3
Coronation 1953	
Souvenir Cards	£2
Coronation Procession	£1
Prince of Wales Investiture 1969	£1.50

H.M. QUEEN ELIZABETH II.

Queen Elizabeth II Colour Photo £4

British Royal £4

OVERSEAS

It will be seen that an equivalent list to the foregoing could be produced for every country in the world which has had a Monarchy at any time since 1869! This remains a vast, uncharted field, where much research is yet to be done. I give below a general guide to price for the Commemorative Souvenir cards already known.

Princess Grace of Monaco Royal wedding R/P £6

Russia

Russian published cards	£25-£35
Continental Publishers	£20-£30
Cartoons	£25
British Publishers	£20-£25

ROYAL EVENTS

1888-1891	£50
1892-1895	£35
1896-1899	£25
1900-1902	£20
1903-1907	£15
1908-1914	£10
1915 onwards	£5

Overseas European royalty, Colour £8

Kaiser £6

Burmese royalty, British published card £8

PORTRAITS

Balkans/Eastern Europe	£8-£12
Belgium/Spain	£3
Other Countries	£6-£10
Weddings	£6

The Art of Shipping

LEYLAND LINE

Above: Cie. des Messageries Maritimes £15
Left: Leyland Line Advert £25
Above Left: NYK Line £12

Up the long stretch of the forest clad coast of Brazil.

Royal Mail Steam Packet Co. £25

SHIPPING

A great number of cards were issued during the early years of the century, and indeed later, perhaps reflecting the dependence which an island nation placed upon the sea. Always a popular theme with collectors, there has been a steady supply of new cards issued on this subject, thanks largely to the many Shipping Companies, who continued publishing throughout the depressed inter-war years, when the flow of more general cards abated.

Market Report; Titanic material continues to fetch staggering prices. Good early advertisng cards and some Kenneth Shoesmith designs have also done well. A location often helps but this is a difficult area for the novice as there are some very attractive but very heavily remaindered cards around.

This is a list of all the shipping Companies known to have published postcards of their ships and routes. This list is not complete, and probably never can be, and will be added to as more information becomes available.To list each Company along with the types of postcards produced by each has therefore become impractical. It would become a catalogue in itself - remembering that there were thousands of shipping companies, that some had hundreds of vessels and that some ships had many postcard images published (of varying scarcity). The result is that it is only practicable to suggest general guide lines as to values in this catalogue. Some ships, like the "Titanic" and "Olympic", will always have more interest. The popular artist-impression postcards are best viewed in Christopher Deakes's "A Postcard History of the Passenger Liner" which has short biographies of many artists. Values of postcard by specific artists are included in the main Artists Section of this Catalogue. Shipbuilding companies from around the world have also published postcards of ships that they have built and, in general these are not so easy to find.

The suggested values are as follows:

Pacific Steam Navigation company poster advert £30

Price guide: No star = low range, 1 star = Mid range & 2 star = Top of range

Chromolithographic advertising	£25-£80
Poster advertising	£20-£60
Japanese inset types	£15
Artist Impressions	£5-£20
Real photographs (officials)	£6-£12
Real photographs	£4-£15
Printed photographs (officials)	£2-£10
Printed photographs	£1-£8
Interiors (artist impressions)	£5-£20
Interiors (photographic)	£3-£8
Japanese ship-launch cards (post war)	£5

We have introduced a star system - No star, One star and two stars - with 2 stars being the higher value. The cards are presumed to be Pre-1939 and in good condition.

Readers should be aware that the rating will depend on the popularity, not necessarily the scarcity, of a company - many people will not have even known that some companies produced cards therefore they do not necessarily have a scarcity value - but good art cards, for example, could influence this. Obviously many cards will be much more common but within these companies there are likely to be ships worth more.

ANCHOR LINE.—TWIN-SCREW STEAMSHIP "CAMERONIA."

Aberdeen line   £20

ABC Steamship Line (GB)*

Aberdeen & Commonwealth Line (GB)

Aberdeen Direct Line (Rennie) (GB)*8

Aberdeen Line (GB)*

Aberdeen Steam Navigation Co (GB)

Aberdeen, Newcastle & Hull (GB)*

Adelaide Steamship (Australia)*

Adler Linie (Germany)

Admiral Line (USA)

Adria Co (Austria/Italy)*

African Steamship Co (GB)

Afrikanische Frucht-Comapgnie (Germany)

Alaska Cruises Inc (USA)

Alaska Steam Ship Co (USA)

Albion Steamship Co (GB)*

Alcoa Steamship Co (USA)

Alexandria Navigation Co (Egypt)

Allan Line (Canada)*

American Banner Line (USA)

American Export Lines (USA)

American Hawaii Cruises (USA)

American Hawaiian Line (USA)

American Line (USA)*

American Mail Lines (USA)

American Merchant Lines (USA)

American Pioneer Line (USA)

American President Lines (USA)

American South African Line (USA)

Anchor Line £8

Amsterdam, Reederij, (Holland)

Anchor Line (GB)

Anchor-Donaldson Line (GB)

Anek Lines (Greece)

Anglo-American Nile & Tourist Co (GB)*

Anglo-Egyptian Mail Line (GB)*

A-O Lines (GB)

Apcar Line (GB)**

Argo Reederei (Germany)*

Arosa Line (Panama)

Athel Line (GB)

Atlantic Steam Navigation Co (GB)

Atlantic Transport Lines (USA)*

Atlanttrafik, AB, (Sweden)

Austasia Line (GB)

Australasian United Steam Navigation (AUSN) (GB)*

Australian Commonwealth Line (Australia)

Australian-Oriental Line (GB)

Australia-West Pacific Line (Norway)

Australind Steam Navigation Co (GB)

Austrian Lloyd (Austria)**

Avenue Shipping (GB)

Aznar Line (Spain)

Bailey & Leetham (GB)**

Baltic American Line (Denmark)**

Baltic State Shipping Line (USSR)

Baltimore & Carolina Steamship Co (USA)

Baltimore Insular Lines (USA)

Baltimore Mail Line (USA)

Baltimore Steam Packet (USA)_

Bank Line (GB)

Barber Lines (Norway)

Barry & Bristol Channel (GB)*

Batavier Line (Holland)

Bateaux ?Moulettes? (France)

Belfast Steamship Co (GB)

Belgian Fruit Lines (Belgium)

Belle Steamers (GB)

Ben Line (GB)

Bennett Line (GB)**

Bergen Line (B&N Line) (Norway)

Bermuda Star Line (USA)

Bibby line £12

Bibby Line (GB)*

Birkenhead Corporation Ferries (GB)

Black Ball Line (Canada)

Black Sea Steamship Line (USSR)

Black Star Line (Ghana)

Bland Line (Gibraltar)*

Blue Funnel Line (GB)**

Blue Star Line (GB)*

Bombay Steam Navigation Co (India)**

Booker Line (GB)

Booth Line (GB)*

Bore Line (Finland)

Bornholm Line (Denmark)

Botel Cruises (Holland)

Bournemouth & South Coast SP Co (GB)

Bowater Steam Ship Co (GB)

Bristol Steam Navigation Co (GB)

British & African Steamship Co (GB)

British Columbia Ferries (Canada)

British India Steam Navigation Co (GB)*

British Petroleum (BP) (GB)

British Tanker Co (GB)

Brodin Line (Sweden)

Broere NV, Gebr., (Holland)

Brostrom Shipping (Sweden)

Brugge-Sluis (Du)

Bruns, W., & Co (Germany)

Bucknall Steamship Lines (GB)*

Bull Lines (USA)

Buries Markes Ltd (GB)

Burns Line (GB)

Burns, Philp & Co (Australia)*

Cairn Line (GB)*

Caledonian Steam Packet Co (GB)

Caltex (World)

Campbell, P&A., (GB)

Canada Steamship Lines (Canada)

Canadian Australasian Line (Can/NZ)

Canadian National Steamships (Canada)

Canadian Northern Steamship (Canada)

Canadian Pacific Steamships (Canada/GB)*

Canguro Linee (Italy)

Cape Cod SS Co (USA)

Caribbean Cruise Lines (USA)

Carnival Cruise Lines (USA)

Carron Line (GB)*

Cassar Co (Malta)**

Castle Line (GB)**

Cawston (GB)

Central Hudson Steamboat (USA)

Cia. Trasatlantica (Spain) £20

Chandris Lines (Greece)

Chemin de Fer du Congo Superior (Belgium)**

Chia. Nacional de Navegacao (Portugal)

Chia. Nacional de Navegacao Costeira (Brazil)**

Chicago Duluth Transit Co (USA)

China Mail Steamship Co (USA)

China Navigation Co (GB)*

Cia. Anonima Venezolana de Navegacion (Venezuela)

Cia. Argentina de Navegacion Dodero (Argentina)

Cia. Maritima Frutera (Spain)

Cia. Transoceanica Argentina (Argentina)*

Cia. Trasatlantica (Spain)*

Cia. Trasmediterranea (Spain)*

Cie. Auxiliaire de Navigation (France)

Cie. de Affreteurs Reunis (France)

Cie. de Navigation Charles le Borgne (France)

Cie. Maritime Belge du Congo £9

Cie. de Navigation Fraissinet & Cyprien Fabre (France)

Cie. de Navigation Mixte (France)

Cie. de Navigation Paquet (France)

Cie. de Navigation Sud-Atlantique (France)

Cie. de Transports Maritimes de l?AOF (France)

Cie. des Chargeurs Reunis (France)

Cie. des Messageries Maritimes (France)*

Cie. Fraissinet (France)

Cie. Generale Transatlantique (France)

Cie. Havraise de Navigation (France)

Cie. Havraise Peninsulaire (France)

Cie. Maritime Belge du Congo (Belgium)*

Cie. Nationale de Navigation (France)

Clyde Shipping £10

Cie. Nationale de Navigation de Grece (Greece)

Cities Service Tankers (USA)

CITRA (Italy)*

City Line (GB)*

City of Cork Steam Packet Co (GB)

City of Dublin Steam Packet Co (GB)*

City Steamboat Co (GB)

Clan Line (GB)

Clarke Steamship Co (Canada)*

Clarkson's Cruises (GB)

Cleveland & Buffalo Line (USA)

Clipper Line (Sweden)

Cunard Line, Aquitania   £25

Clyde Line (USA)*

Clyde Shipping Co (GB)*

Clyde-Mallory Line (USA)

Coast Lines (GB)

Cogedar Line (Italy)

Colombian Line (USA)*

Colonial Navigation Co (USA)

Colwyn Bay & Liverpool SS Co (GB)**

Common Brothers (GB)

Commonwealth & Dominion Line (GB)

Concordia Line (Norway)

Constantine Line (GB)

Cook's Tourist Steamers (GB)

Corsica Ferries (Italy)

Cory, William, & Son (GB)

Cosens & Co (GB)

Costa Line (Italy)

Crescent Shipping Lines (Pakistan)

Cunard Line (GB)

Cunard White Star (GB)

Currie Line (GB)

Cusolich Line (Austria/Italy)*

Dairen Kisen Kaisha (Japan)*

Dalen, Rederi, (Sweden)

Dansk-Statsbaner (DSB) (Denmark)

De la Rama Lines (USA)

Deilmann, Peter, (Germany)

Delta Line (USA)

Denholm, J&J, Ltd (GB)

Detroit & Cleveland Line (USA)

Deutsche Eisenbahn (Germany)

Deutsche Levante Linie (Germany)

Deutsche Ost-Afrika Linie (Germany)**

Deutsche Seereederie (East Germany)

DFDS (Denmark)

Di Giorgio SS Line (USA)*

Direct Line (GB)*

Doeksen, Reederij,

Dollar Steamship Lines (USA)

Donaldson Line   £8

Dominion Far East Line (GB)

Dominion Line (GB)

Donaldson Line (GB)

Drake Shipping Co (GB)

Dublin & Manchester Line (GB)*

Dublin & Silloth Line (GB)*

Dubrovacka Parobrodska Plovidba (Yugoslavia)

Dundee & Newcastle Steam Shipping (GB)*

Dundee, Perth & London Shipping Co (GB)**

East African Railways (GB)*

Eastern & Australian Line (GB)*

Eastern Mediterranean Express Line (GB)*

Eastern Shipping Corporation (India)

Egyptian Mail Steamship Lines (GB)**

Egyptian Shipping Co (GB)

Elder Dempster Lines £12

Elder Dempster Lines (GB)

Elders & Fyffes(GB)*

Ellerman & Bucknall Steamships (GB)

Ellerman & Papayanni Lines (GB)*

Ellerman Lines (GB)

Ellerman's City Line (GB)

Ellerman's Hall Line (GB)

Ellerman's Wilson Line (GB)

ELMA (Argentina)

Empresa Insulana de Navegacao (Portugal)

Enkhuizen-Stavoren (Holland)

Enterprise Transportation Co (USA)

Epirotiki Line (Greece)

Epirus Line (Greece)

Erste Donau (Austria)

Ertslijn (Holland)

Esso Petroeum (international)

Europe Canada Line (Panama)

Europe-Australia Line (Greece)

Euxine Shipping (GB)

Everard, F.T.., & Sons (GB)

Fabre Line (France)

Fall River Line (USA)

FANU (Argentina)*

Far-Eastern Steamship Co (USSR)

Farrell Lines (USA)

Fearnley & Eger (Norway)

Federal Steam Navigation (GB)

Ferrovie dello Stato (Italy)*

FHS (Federal-Houlder-Shire) (GB)*

Finland Steamship Co (Finland)*

Finska Angfartygs Aktiebolaget (Finland)*

Fisher, Renwick & Co (GB)

Flota Argentina de Navegacion de Ultramar (FANU) (Argentina)*

Flota Mercante del Estado (Argentina)*

Flotta Lauro (Italy)

Flushing Line (Holland)

Fragline (Greece)

France, Fenwick & Co (GB)*

Fratelli Grimaldi Armatori (Italy)

Fraternitas, Rederi, (Sweden)

French Line (CGT) (France)

Fritzen & Sohn, Johs., (Germany)

Furness Bermuda Line (GB)

Ellerman Line £12

142

Furness Line £12

Furness Lines (GB)*

Fyffes (GB)*

Gdynia-America Line (Poland)

General Steam Navigation Co (GB)

Glen Line (GB)*

Goodrich Transit Co (USA)

Gorthon Lines (Sweden)

Gota Kanal Rederi (Sweden)

Goteborg-Frederikshavn Linjen (Sweden)

Gothabolaget (Sweden)

Gotland, Angfartygs Ab, (Sweden)

Grace Line (USA)

Grand Trunk Pacific Steamship (Canada)

Grangesbergsbolaget (Sweden)

Great Lakes Transit Corporation USA)

Great Northern Pacific SS Co (USA)

Greek Australian Line (Greece)

Greek Line (Greece)

Grimaldi-Siosa Line (Italy)

Hamburg Amerika Line £25

Gulf Line (GB)**

Haaland (Norway)

Hadag (Germany)

Hafen Dampschiff. AG (Germany)

Haj Line (India)**

Hall?s Line (GB)

Hamburg & Anglo-American Nile Co

Hamburg-Amerika Linie (Germany)**

Hamburg-Atlantic Linie (Germany)

Hamburg-Bremer-Afrika Linien (Germany)

Hamburg-Sudamerika Linie (Germany)*

Hansa, Deutsche Dampfschiff, Gesell. (Germany)

HAPAG (Germany)

Hapag-Lloyd (Germany)

Harrison, T&J., Line (GB)

Havenlijn (Holland)

General Steam Navigation Line £10

Hawaiian Steamship Co (USA)

Hellenic Mediterranean Lines (Greece)

Helsingborg, Rederi Aktiebolaget, (Sweden)

Henderson Line (GB)*

Holland Afrika Line (Holland)

Holland Friesland Lijn (Holland)

Holland Ireland Line (Holland)

Holland Steamship Co (Holland)

Holland Veluwe Lijn (Holland)

Holland West-Afrika Lijn (Holland)

Holland-Amerika Lijn (Holland)

Holt, John, Line (GB)

Home Lines (Panama)

Hong Kong, Canton & Macau Steamboat (GB)**

Horn Linie (Germany)

Hough Line (GB)*

Houlder Line (GB)

Howard Smith Ltd (Australia)*

Huddard, Parker (Australia)

Hudson Navigation Co (USA)

Hudson River Day Line (USA)

Iberian Star Line (Panama)

Imperial Department Railways (Japan)

Imperial Direct West India Mail (GB)**

Incres Line (USA)*

Independent Gulf Line (Holland)

Indiana Transport (USA)

Indiana Transportation Co (USA)

Indo-China Steam Navigation Co (GB)*

Instone Line (GB)*

Inter-Island Steam Navigation Co (USA)

Intourist (USSR)

Irish Shipping Ltd (Ireland)

Irrawaddy Flotilla Co (GB)**

Isbrandtsen Lines (USA)

Island Tug & Barge (Canada)

Islands Steamship (Iceland)*

Isle of Man Steam Packet Co (GB)

Isles of Scilly SS Co (GB)

Italia Line (Soc. Per Azioni di Navigazione) (Italy)

Ivaran Lines (Norway)

Jadranska Plovidba (Yugoslavia)

Jakob Lines (Finland)

Jamaica Banana Producers SS Co (GB)*

Japan Line (Japan)

Japanese Railways (Japan)

Jardine   Mathison (GB)*

Johnson Line (Sweden)

Johnston Warren Lines (GB)

Jugoslavenski Lloyd (Yugoslavia)

Karageorgis Lines (Greece)

Kavounides Line (Greece)

KdF (Germany)*

Khedivial Mail Line (GB)**

Kingsin Linie (Germany)**

Kinkai Yusen   KK (Japan)

Knutsen Line (Norway)

Kokusai Kisen Kaisha (Japan)*

Koln-Dusseldorfer (Germany)

Koln-Dusseldorfer Rheindamfschiffahrt (Germany)

Kolokotronis Lines (Greece)

Koninklijke Hollandsche Lloyd (Holland)

Holland America Line £12

144

JAVA-CHINA-JAPAN LIJN

Kon Java-China Pakepvaart Line £24

Koninklijke Java-China Pakepvaart Lijnen (Holland)

Koninklijke Nederlandsche Stoomboot Maats (KNSM) (Holland)

Koninklijke Paketvaart Maats (KPM) (Holland)*

Koninklijke Rotterdamsche Lloyd (Holland)

Kosmos Linie (Germany)**

Kreisschiffahrt (Germany)

Kriton Shipping (Greece)

La Veloce (Italy)*

Laegterkompaniet (Norway)

Laeisz, F., (Germany)

Lamey Tugs (GB)

Lamport & Holt Line (GB)*

Langlands & Sons (GB)

Lassman (Russia)**

Lauritzen, J., (Denmark)

Lauro Lines (Italy)

Leonhardt & Blimberg (Germany)

Price guide: No star = low range, 1 star =

Leyland Line (GB)**

Libra Maritime (Greece)

Lindblad Travel (USA)

Linea 'C' (Italy)

Lineas Maritimas Argentinas (ELMA) (Argentina)*

Liverpool& North Wales Steamship Co (GB)*

Lloyd Austriaco (Austria)**

Lloyd Brazileiro (Brazil)**

Lloyd Genovese (Italy)*

Lloyd Italiano (Italy)

Lloyd Royal Belge (Belgium)*

Lloyd Sabaudo (Italy)*

Lloyd Triestino (Italy)

London & Edinburgh Shipping Co (GB)

London & Overseas Freighters (GB)

London County Council (GB)

London Missionary Society (GB)

Los Angeles Steamship Co (USA)

Lubeck Linie (Germany)

Lund's Blue Anchor Line (GB)**

Lykes Bros. Steamship Co (USA)

Lyle Shipping Co (GB)

MacAndrews & Co (GB)

MacBrayne, David, Ltd (GB)*

MacIver Line (GB)

Maersk Line (Denmark)

Lauro Line Italy £5

145

Lund's Blue Anchor Line £30

Manchester Liners (GB)

Metcalf Motor Coasters (GB)

Marittima Italiana (Italy)

Matson Navigation Co (USA)*

McIlwraith, McEarcharn Line (Australia)

Mediterranean Sun Line Lines (Greece)

Melbourne Steamship Line (Australia)

Merchants & Miners Transportation Co (USA)*

Mersey Docks & Harbour Board (GB)

Messina, Ignacio, &Co (Italy)

Meyer Line (Norway)

Miami Steamship Co (USA)

Military Sea Transportation Service (USA)

Mitsui Line (Japan)*

Mitsui OSK Lines (Japan)

Mobil (international)

Mogul Line (India)*

Monticello SS Co (USA)

Moore-McCormack Lines (USA)

Morgan Line (USA)

Morocco, Canary Islands & Madeira Line (GB)*

Mory & Cie (France)

Moss Hutchinson (GB)

Moss Steamship (GB)*

Muller, Wm.H., & Co (Holland)

Munson Steamship Co (USA)

Murmansk Shipping Co (USSR)

Muskoka Navigation Co (Canada)

Naias Shipping (Greece)

Natal Line (GB)*

National Hellenic American Line (Greece)

Nautilus Steam Shipping Co (GB)

Naviera Aznar (Spain)

Naviera de Exportacion (Spain)

Naviera Pinillos (Spain)*

Navigazione Generale Italiana (NGI) (Italy)*

Navigazione Libera Triestina (Italy)

Navigazione sul Lago di Garda (Italy)

Nederland Line (Holland)

Nederlandse Tank & Paketvaart Maats (Holland)

Nelson Line (GB)*

Neptun Dampfs. (Germany)

New Bedford, Martha's Vineyard etc (USA)

New Medway Steam Packet Co (GB)

New Palace Steamers (GB)

New York & Cuba Mail (USA)*

New York & Porto Rico SS Co (USA)*

New Zealand Shipping Co (GB)

Niagara Navigation Co (Canada)

Nicholson Erie-Dover Line (Canada)

Niederland Dampfs. Rhederei (Holland)

Nihonkai Kisen Kaisha (Japan)

Nippon Enkai Ferry (Japan)

Nippon Yusen Kaisha (Japan)*

Nobiling, Reederei, (Germany)

Matson Line Co. £12

Price guide: No star = low range, 1 star =

Nomikos Lines (Greece)

Norddeutscher Lloyd (Germany)**

Nordenfjeldske Damps. (Norway)

Nordsee Linie (Germany)

Norfolk & Washington Steamboat Co (USA)

Norske Amerikalinje (Norway)*

North Coast Steam Navigation Co (Australia)

Osaka Shosen Kaisha Line £15

Norddeutscher Lloyd Line £15

North of Scotland, Orkney & Shetland Shipping (GB)*

Northern Michigan Transportation (USA)

Northern Navigation Co (Canada)

Northern Steamship Co (New Zealand)

Northland Shipping Co (Canada)

Northland Steamship Co (USA)

Norwegian Asia Line (Norway)

Norwegian Caribbean Lines (Norway)

Ocean Steamship Co of Savannah (USA)

Oceanic Steamship Co (USA)

Old Bay Line (USA)

Old Dominion Line (USA)*

Oldenburg-Portugiesische Damps (Germany)

Olsen, Fred., & Co (Norway)*

Olympic Cruises (Greece)

Orient Lines (GB)

Orient Overseas Line (Hong Kong)

Orient Steam Navigation (GB)

Orient-Pacific Line (GB)

Orient-Royal Mail Line (GB)

Orkney Islands Shipping Co (GB)

Osaka Shosen Kaisha (Japan)**

Ostasiatiske Kompagni (Denmark)

Ostend-Dover Line (Belgium)

Ozean Linie (Germany)*

P&O (GB)

P&O Branch Service (GB)

PAAK (Pakistan)

Pacific Coast Steamships (USA)

Pacific Far East Line (USA)

Pacific Mail Line (USA)

Pacific Shipowners

Pacific Steam Navigation Co (GB)**

Pacific Steamship Co (Admiral Line) (USA)

Pacific Transport Line (USA)

Palm Line (GB)*

Panama Mail Steamship (USA)

Panama Railroad (USA)*

Orient Line £5

Nancy sends you her best love & a big kiss and thanks you very much for the nice book you have sent her for Christmas.

PacificMail £10

Panama Steamship Line (USA)*

Panama-Pacific Line (USA)

Pan-Islamic Steamship Co (Pakistan)*

Peninsular & Occidental Steamship (P&O) (USA)

Peninsular & Oriental Steam Navigation (P&O) (GB)

Plant Line (Canada)*

Polish Ocean Lines (Poland)

Polish-British Steamship Co (Poland)*

Polytechnic Cruising Association (GB)*

Port Jackson & Manly Steamship Co (Australia)

Port Line (GB)

Porto Rico Line (USA)*

Poseidon Schiffahrt (Germany)

Powell Line (GB)*

Presthus Rederi, Johs., (Norway)

Primorsk Shipping Co (USSR)

Prince Line (GB)

Princess Cruise Lines (USA)

Prinzenlinien (Germany)

Provinciale Stoomboot (Holland)

Prudential Lines (USA)

Puget Sound Line (USA)

Purfina (France)

Quebec Steamship (GB)**

Queensboro & Flushing Line (Holland)

R&O Navigation (Canada)

Ragne, Rederiaktiebolaget, (Sweden)

Rankine Line (GB)**

Red Funnel Line (GB)*

Red Star Line (Belgium/USA)*

Regency Cruises

Rennie Line (GB)*

Reut, Rederi AB, (Sweden)

Rickmers Linie (Germany)*

Ropner & Co (GB)

Roumanian State Service (Roumania)**

Royal Cruise Line (Greece)

Royal Hungarian River & Sea Navigation (Hungary)*

Royal Line (Canada)

Royal Mail Steam Packet/Lines (GB)

Royal Netherlands West-India Mail (Holland)**

Royal Viking Line (Norway)

Russian Volunteer Fleet **

Russian Steam Navigation & Trade (Russia)**

P & O Line £15

Royal Mail Steam Packet Co. £20

Russian-American Line (Russia)*

Sachsisch-Bohmischen Dampfs. Ges (Germany)

Sacor Maritima (Portugal)

Salenrederierma (Sweden)

Saltash, Three Towns & District Steamboat

Salter (GB)

San Francisco & Portland Steamship (USA)

Saturnus, Rederi, (Sweden)

Savannah Line (USA)

Scandinavian American Line (Denmark)*

Schuppe, Victor, Reederei, (Germany)

Scottish Shire Line (GB)*

Seas Shipping (USA)

Sessan Line (Sweden)

Setsuyo Shosen Kaisha (Japan)

SGTM (France)

Shaw, Savill & Albion Co (GB)

Shin Nihonkai (Japan)

Sidarma Line (Italy)

Silja Line (Scandinavia)

Silver Star Line (USA)**

Siosa Line (Italy)

SITMAR (Soc. Italiana de Services) (Italy)*

Sitmar Line (Italy)

Skou, Ove, (Denmark)

Sloan & Co (GB)*

Smit, L., & Co's Internationale Sleepdienst (Holland)

Soc. 'Italia' (Italy)

Soc. Algerienne de Navigation (France)

Soc. di Navigazione 'Puglia' (Italy)*

Soc. di Navigazione 'San Marco' (Italy)*

Soc. di Navigazione 'Sicilia' (Italy)

Soc. di Navigazione a Vapore Italia (Italy)*

Soc. di Navigazione per Azione 'Italnavi' (Italy)

Soc. Generale de Transports Maritimes (France)

Soc. Geral de Comercio (Portugal)

Soc. Italiana de Servicei (Italy)

Soc. Italiana Servizi Maritime (Italy)

Soc. les Affreteurs Reunis (France)*

Soc. Maritime Nationale (France)

Soc. Misr de Navigation (Egypt)*

Soc. Napoletana di Navigazione e Vapore (Italy)

Soc. Navale de l'Ouest (Fr)

Soc. Partenopea di Navigazione (Italy)

Soc. per Azione di Navigazione 'Italia' (Italy)

Soc. per Azioni di Navigazione 'Tirrenia' (Italy)

Somerfin Passenger Lines (Israel)

South American Saint Line (GB)

Southampton, Isle of Wight & South of England SP (GB)*

Southampton, Isle of Wight & South of England £12

Shaw Savill Line £15

Southern Pacific Railroad (USA)

Southern Pacific Steamship (USA)

Soviet Danube Steamship Line (USSR)

St. Petersburg Express Line (Russia)**

Stag Line (GB)

Standard Fruit & Steamship Co (USA)

State Shipping Service (Australia)

States Steamship Co (USA)

Stena Line (Sweden)

Stettiner Damfercompagnie (Germany)

Stinnes, Hugo, (Germany)*

Stockholms Rederi AB Svea (Sweden)

Sudan Government Steamers (Sudan)*

Sun Line (Greece)

Sun Tugs (GB)

Svea Line (Sweden)

Svenska Amerika Line (Sweden)

Svenska Lloyd (Sweden)

Svenska Orient Linien (Sweden)

Svenska Rederiaktiebolaget Oresund (Sweden)

Swadeshi Steam Navigation Co (India)**

Swedish-Chicago Line (Sweden)

Taiyo Ferry KK (Japan)

Tasmanian Steamers (Australia)

Taya Line (Spain)**

Tedcastle, McCormick & Co (GB)**

Terukuni Kaiun Kaisha (Japan)

Testa, Bernadino, (Italy)

Thorden Line (Sweden)

Thule Line (Sweden)

Tintore Line (Spain)**

Tirrenia Line (Italy)

Toho Kaiun Kaisha (Japan)

Tokai Line (Japan)

Tor Line (Sweden)

Torm Lines (Denmark)

Townsend Bros. Ferries (GB)

Toyas, John, (Greece)**

Toyo Kisen Kaisha (Japan)

Toyo Yusen (Japan)

Transatlantic, Rederiaktiebolaget, (Sweden)

Transatlantica Italiana (Italy)**

Transmarin Aktiebolaget (Sweden)

Transports Maritimes Est-Tunisien (France)

Traunsee Dampfschiffahrt (Austria)

Swedish Lloyd Line £15

Turkish Maritime Line £5

Trinder, Anderson & Co (GB)

Turbine Steamers Ltd (GB)

Turkish Maritime Lines (Turkey)

Turnbull, Martin & Co (GB)

Turnbull, Scott & Co (GB)

Tyne General Ferry Co (GB)*

Tyne-Tees Shipping Co (GB)*

Typaldos Lines (Greece)*

Ullswater Navigation & Transit Co (GB)

Union Steam Ship(GB)**

Union Steamship Co (Canada)

Union Steamship Co of New Zealand (GB/NZ)*

Union Sulphur Co (USA)

Union-Castle Line (GB)**

United American Lines (USA)

United Arab Maritime Co (Egypt)

United Baltic Lines (GB)

United Fruit Lines (USA)

United States Forces (USA)

United States Lines (USA)

Uranium Steamship Co (GB)**

USSR State Shipping Companies, Morflot etc (USSR)

Vaccaro Line (USA)

Van Nievelt, Goudriaan & Co (Holland)

Van Ommeren, Phs., NV (Holland)

Vereeigde Nederlandsche Scheepvaart (Holland)

Vierwaldstatersee (Switzeralnd)

Viking Cruises (Italy)

Woermann Line £18

Viking Cruising Co (GB)*

Villain & Fassio (Italy)*

Virginia Ferry (USA)

Volga Steam Navigation Co (Russia)

Vriesvaart Maats. (Holland)

Wagenborg's Scheep. (Holland)

Walleniusrederierna (Sweden)

Ward Line (USA)*

Warnemunde-Gedser Linie (Germany)

Warren Line (GB)**

Waterman Steamship Corporation (USA)

Union Steamship Co of New Zealand £16

White Star Line £12

Watts, Watts & Co (GB)

Waxholms Nya Angf. (Sweden)

West Line (USA)

White Star Line (GB)**

Wilhelmsen Lines (Norway)

Williamson's Turbine Steamers (GB)

Wilson Line (GB)**

Woermann Linie (Germany)*

Ybarra & Cia (Spain)*

Yeoward Line (GB)*

Zeeland Line (Holland)

Zim Israel Lines (Israel)

Zim Line £12

FAMOUS LINERS
Lusitania R.M.S.

Sketches of Disaster	£8
Art/Photographic	£8-20
In Memoriam	£15

Celebrated Liners/Tuck R.

Oilette Series/20+ Sets	£6-12

Miscellaneous Liners
Pre-1939

/Coloured	£5-20
/Real Photographic	£4-15
1940 onwards	£4-10
Interiors	£3-10
Hoffman C./Southampton	£5-10
F.G.O. Stuart	£5-10

Titanic R.M.S.

Building/Harland & Woolf	£100+
Ship's anchor in transport	£100+
Leaving Southampton 1912	£90+
Passengers in `Carpathia' lifeboats	£150+
Other related pre-disaster cards	£90+
'Nearer my God to Thee'/Set 3/4.	
Pub. Bamforth. Price per card	£20

The cards listed above are all genuine `Titanic' and mainly real photographic in style. As such they are worth considerably more than other `Titanic' cards listed below, which are usually re-titled versions of her sister ship `Olympic', often overprinted with details of the disaster. The reason for this is that the `Titanic' went down before the majority of publishers got round to photographing her, so they substituted existing pictures of the almost identical `Olympic'. One can tell the difference in that the real `Titanic' had a closed superstructure while that on the `Olympic' was open.

In Memoriam/Bragg E.A.	£50
National Series	£50
RP/Printed Photographic	£35+
Art Types	£30+

Associated Ships

Britannic (Sister ship/4 funnels)	£40
Carpathia	£50
Olympic	£15-35

MISCELLANEOUS PHOTOGRAPHIC

Cable Ships	£5-10
Cargo Ships	£5-15
Cruise Ships	£1-6
Hospital Ships	£12-30
Houseboats	£5
Icebreakers	£10-15
Launchings	£15-30
Lightships	£12-5
On-board-ship scenes	£-10
Pleasure Boats	£3-7
Speedboats	£8-12
Tankers	£3-12
Troopships	£8-12

Convict Ships

At named locations	£15
Unlocated	£6

Twin-Screw Steamship YUCATAN · El Vapor YUCATAN de dos helices

Ward Line £10

Interior Studies	£5
Divers	
Naval	£5-15
Civilian	£15
Winchester Diver	£18
Docks/Harbours/Ports	
Construction/Southampton	£40
Construction/Immingham	£20
Spectacular RP Views	£30
General scenes	£3-10
Ferries	
Cross Channel	£3-10
Steam Ferries	£3-10
Floating Bridges	£8
Rowing Boats	£5
Lifeboats	
`Inland Launchings'	£35
Advertising Posters RNLI	£35
Lifeboat Saturday Parades	£35
Close-up Studies	£20
Crews/Portraits	£18
Parades	£28
Coastguards/Stations	£10
Lighthouses	
GB Locations	£2-10
Foreign Locations	£3-5
Paddle Steamers	
GB	£4-15
Overseas	£4-10
Rhine Steamers	£3-10
Swiss Lake Steamers	£2-5
Royal Yachts	
GB	£2-5
Foreign	£2-8
Sailing Ships	
Barges	£5-15
Coastal	£5-10
Ocean	£5-10
Shipyards	
Cammell Laird	£8+

Olympic, Tuck Oilette series £20

Harland & Woolf	£5-10
Ship under construction	£10-20
Yards miscellaneous	£5-20
Tugs	
Paddle	£7-12
Officials	£8-20
Others	£5-10
Whaling Industry	
Hebrides/Factory scenes	£45
Ships/General Views	£10-25
Stations/Factory Scene	£30
Washed up/Stranded	£5-18
Ships	£18
Wrecks	
HMS Montagu	£5-25
Submarine at Hastings	£10-15
SS Mahratta	£5-15
Other Wrecks	£10-20
Yachts	
Americas Cup	£5-10
Racing	£2-6

Shipwreck of The Media £12

SILK CARDS

The earliest cards of this type were Woven Silks which originated in Germany in 1898. The main manufacturers were H.M. Krieger and Rudolf Knuffman. Shortly afterwards in 1903 the Coventry based firms of Thomas Stevens and W.H. Grant began making similar cards in this country, while at around the same time Neyret Freres commenced manufacturing Woven Silks in France.

Embroidered Silks first appeared in 1900, although it was not until the First World War that they reached the height of their popularity. The basic difference between the two types is that Woven Silks were machine made, and consequently of uniform finish, whereas Embroidered silks were mainly produced on hand looms, leaving a raised surface where the threads may be clearly seen, with often irregular variations in design from card to card.

The RF Catalogue 1985 contains a comprehensive listing by Chris Radley of all the main Woven and Embroidered Silk card types.

Market Report

This is a specialized market where prices tend to be determined at auction for the rarer types. Condition is paramount. There is a steady demand for WW1 patriotic examples from the general antique trade at current price levels.

WOVEN

STEVENS T.

Experimental Types	£90
Portraits	£60+
Religious Subjects	£40
Views	£25+
General Subjects	£25+

Ships

Titanic	£750
Battleships	£90+
Transports	£60
Liners, Steamers and Landing Stages	£40+
Hands Across the Sea	£30+

Hands across the sea £40

R.M.S. CARONIA.
21000 tons.   676 feet long.   72 feet 6in. broad.

Above; Woven Silk, Liner £40

Alpha Series

(Designs produced by Stevens for Alpha Publishing Co.)

Greetings	£25
Flags	£25+
Stevens Designs	£30+

GRANT W.H.

Exhibitions	£40+
Portraits	£40+
Subjects	£35+
Hands Across the Sea /	
Ships and Greetings	£35+
Greetings from	£30+
Greetings, Songs and Hymns	£35
Views	£20+

Above; WW1 patriotic portrait £50

Above; French WW1 patriotic portrait £40

FRANCE
A. Benoiston

Paris Exposition 1900	£150
Others	£40

Neyret Freres
1903-1904

Art Nouveau/Paintings/Portraits	£50+

1905-1914

Art Nouveau/Portraits/Views	£50+

1907-1918

Religion/Paintings	£30+

1915-1917

WW1 Patriotic/Portraits	£25+

1917-1918

WW1 Patriotic/Portraits	£25+

1916-1919

Flames	£20+

1917-1918

Sentimental Greetings	£25

Bertrand and Boiron 1915-1916

WW1 Portraits/Religion	£50+

Others 1930-1945	£12+

GERMANY

H.M. Kreiger	£30+
Rudolf Knuffman/1898-1905	£30+
Nazi Interest/1936-1938	£50+
Others/1899-1915	£25+

OTHER EUROPEAN

Austria/1900-1939	£25+
Switzerland/1900-1910	£25+
Czechoslovakia/1916-1938	£12+

JAPAN

Views and Portraits	£40
With Copy of Grant Mount	£50

U.S.A.

1904 Exposition	£200
Set 14	£2000
Others	£30+

PRINTED SILK/SATIN

Flames//Edition Gabriel	£20
Kitchener Lord	£20
Stewart & Woolf Series	£15
Regiments/Countries	£15
Miscellaneous	£8

H.M. Krieger

Four Seasons Set	£200
Others	£30

Cavell Edith

In original D.M. envelope	£6
Card only	£4

Cinema Stars/Plain Backs

Transatlantic Films	£3

FAB PATCHWORK CARDS
W.N. SHARPE/BRADFORD

Actresses	£15
Royalty	£15
Views	£12
Heraldic	£12
Flowers	£12
PAT.735 (Gaunt Armley)	£12

EMBROIDERED/WW1
REGIMENTAL BADGES

Household Cavalry	£40
Cavalry of the Line	£60
Cavalry Special Reserve Units	£60
Yeomanry Regiments	£60
Royal Regiment of Artillery	
British Regiments	£35
Overseas Regiments	£50
Foot Guards	£50
Infantry of the Line	£50
Territorial Force	
Independent Units	£50
London Regiments	£40
Expeditionary Forces	
Britain/France	£40
Australasia	£40
Canada/USA	£50
Divisional Corps	£40
British Army Corps	
British Corps/ASC.RE.RFA, etc.	£12
Overseas Corps	£40
Overseas Regiments	£75
Royal Navy	
Units	£50
Ships	£50
Royal Navy	£40
Royal Naval Air Service	£50
Royal Air Force	
Royal Flying Corps	£50
Royal Air Force	£45
Independent Organisations	
Red Cross/Salvation Army etc.	£50

The whole field of WW1 Embroidered Silk Cards is vast and complex, with literally thousands of different designs covered under the three columns of this listing. Many of these cards are very scarce, in some cases only one copy being known. This catalogue can only offer a general guide to type and price.

East Yorks Regiment £50

LEADERS/STATESMEN/ROYALTY

Inset Photos/Single	£20
Inset Photos/Doubles	£25
Names/WW1 Leaders	£25

HERALDIC

Overseas Towns	£40
Overseas Countries/Islands	£25
European Towns	£15
European Countries	£15
English Towns	£30
England/Scotland/Wales	£25
Ireland/Eire/Shamrock Isle	£25

Birn Brothers/With Printed Title

Overseas Towns	£25
European Towns	£20
English Towns	£20

YEAR DATES

1914-1919	£10
1920-1923	£15
1925-1939	£18
1940	£10
1945	£15

SENTIMENTAL GREETINGS/
HEARTS & FLOWERS TYPE
Flag/Patriotic £8
Sentimental Greetings £5
Many cards of this type were made in the form of an Envelope. If such a card still contains its original insert, the following premium may be added to the prices above:

Silk Handkerchief	£3
Artist signed	£1
Celluloid	£1
War Scenes	£1
Perfumed	£1

BETTER DESIGNS

Advertising	£50
Aircraft/Guns etc.	£15
Army Camps	£25
Buildings	£20
Cartoons	£20
Cathedrals	£20
Cathedrals in Flames	£15
Cats	£18
Colonial Exhibition	£40
English Buildings	£30
Father Xmas/Girls etc	£25
Flower Baskets	£8
Pan-Pacific Exhibition 1915	£40
Personal Names	£15
Saints	£15
Soldiers/Sailors/Medals etc	£25
War Destruction	£15
Zeppelins	£20

To qualify for listed price the image must be the dominant feature of the card. A tiny Cat or small Building will not do!

EMBROIDERED/
MISCELLANEOUS
Birn Bros.

Printed Regimental Badges	£20
Flowers	£8

Tuck R. & Sons
Broderie D'Art series £6

Spanish Embroidery

Early cards	£6
Later	£3
Modern	£1.50

Spanish Silk, later issue £3

Basket of flowers design £8

SPORT

One of the subjects which enjoys a popularity today at least equal to that of the Edwardian period, when Sporting cards filled every album. Always a good collecting area with a very wide variety of cards, where prices have been subject to continued and steady growth over the years.

Market Report
Cricket grounds seem to be following football stadiums up the price table. Wrestling and bodybuilding are making a comeback. Boxing has had a little bounce back, Cricket, Golf and Football cards have to be scarce to make the higher prices. Look out for good athletics as a possible investment.

ANGLING
Comic Sketches	£3
Miscellaneous	£4

ARCHERY
Competitions	£10
Miscellaneous	£5

ATHLETICS
Meetings	£15
Athletes/Named	£15
Stadiums	£12

BADMINTON
Miscellaneous	£8

BASEBALL
Players	£5/£15
Comic Sketches	£10/£18
Stadiums	£5/ £12

BASKETBALL/NETBALL
Miscellaneous	£4

BILLIARDS/SNOOKER
Players/Named Photographic Pro	£45
Players/General	£10
Billiard Halls	£8-£15
Comic Sketches	£8/12

Boxer, Archie Moore £15

BOWLS
Miscellaneous	£4

BOXING
Famous Boxers/Beagles Ltd.	£15
Professional Boxing	£12-£20
Jack Johnson	£25
Amateur Boxing	£5

BULLFIGHTING
Art Studies	£2
Photographic	£3

CAVES/CAVING
Miscellaneous	£2

Billiard Hall £12

BOARD GAMES
Chess	£15-£20
Other games	£3

Cycle racing, Harry Grant, world Cycle Champion Photo c.1929   £25

CRICKET

County/International Players	£18
W.G.Grace	£30
Donald Bradman	£25
County Grounds	£15
Comic Sketches	£8/£15

Teams

County Teams	£15-20
International Teams	£15-20
Star Series	£6
National Series	£15
Amateur Teams/ Identified	£5

Australian touring side, 1934, £20

CROQUET
Miscellaneous	£6

CURLING
Miscellaneous	£3

CYCLE RACING
Tour de France/Portraits	£20
Tour de France/Pre 1939	£25
Personalities/Events/Pre 1939	£20-£25
/Post 1939	£10

FENCING
Miscellaneous	£6

FOOTBALL
LEAGUE TEAMS
Series

Rapid Photographic series	£50
Famous Football Teams/	
Wrench Series 107...(Names)	£50+
Oxo Advertising Cards	£60+
London Football Teams/	
B&B Series G11/Coloured	£40
Ozograph Series/Bristol	£50
Rotary Photographic/Series 3844	£50+
Health & Strength	£45
Misch & Co "Football Teams"	£40

Miscellaneous

Football League/Bw photographic	£45-75
/Bw printed	£40-50
Olympic Teams	£15/£30

Prices for League Teams are governed largely by the status of the team itself. e.g. Man. Utd. is worth more than Barnsley.

Players

Wrench Series 21../29../c.1903	£45
Benefit Cards/Football League	£30-£45
Bw photographic	£35
Tuck Famous football players	£40
Birmingham Novelty Co 'Football' series	£50
C.W.Faulkner &co	£45
"Herriot" series	£45

MISCELLANEOUS

Wembley Cup Final 1923/Campbell Gray/	
Commemorative Set 3/With Packet	£140
/Without packet	£80
Arsenal Cartoon/Kentish Independent	£45
International Teams	£40
Football Series 940/c.1903	
Tuck R. & Sons	£40
In Memoriam Cards/In Memory of/	
b/w Comic Sketches	£30
Football League Stadiums	£45-£75
Football Stadiums Overseas	£15
Football Colours/Frank Reynolds/	
Comic Sketches	£15
Non-League Teams/Semi-Pro	£15
Amateur Teams/Identified	£6-12
/Unidentified	£4
Crowd scenes/Brighton/F. Wiles	£10-15
/Miscellaneous	£10
Comic Sketches	£8

Millwall, R/P Early professional team groups similar to this one can sell for £50+. The price depends on the demand for the card.

GOLF

Left: shows a privately published R/P postcard of Henry Cotton £50

Wrench Series/Players/ Bw undivided back	£150+
Players Known/Named	£50 - £140
Pro Tournaments	£120+
Club Houses	£8/£20
Championship Courses	£15-£35
Courses	£5/£8
Comic Sketches	£8/£15

Golf Advert Cards

Poster Type	£70
Product Advertising	£20-£40

GREYHOUND RACING

Tracks interior	£15-£20
Named Dogs R/P	£12

White City Stadium, showing dog track £18

GYMNASTICS

Miscellaneous	£3

HOCKEY

International teams	£12
Miscellaneous	£3-£8

HURLING

Team groups	£15

HORSE SHOWS/JUMPING

Int. Horse Show/Product Advert	£8
Show Jumping/Riders	£5
General Scenes	£3

HORSE RACING

Jockeys	£8-15
Race Horses	£7.50

Race Courses

Doncaster/York etc./ Printed multi-view type	£4
In current use	£6-£8

Pre-1939

Gatwick	£70
Lewes	£50
RP studies	£20
Printed/Goodwood etc.	£8
Abandoned	£15

Courses where Racing was abandoned long ago are worth more than those in current use.

Series

B & D/Kromo Series	£12
Bird H./Everett's Series	£12
Meissner & Buch Series 1003	£15
Tuck R./Derby Winners	£15
Tuck R./Popular Racing Colours	£15
Walker J./Celebrated Racers	£15
Wildt & Kray/Racing Colours	£15
Wrench Series	£15

LACROSSE

Team groups UK R/P	£18
Team groups OVERSEAS	£12

The Capitals Lacrosse Team £18

MOTOR RACING

Paris-Madrid Road Race 1903	£35
L'Hirondelle Series	£20
Peking-Paris	£20
French Drivers c.1905/	
Pub. J. Bouveret/Le Mans	£20
European Circuits	£12-£20
Valentine's R/P racing car series	£7

Brooklands

Action/Portraits	£20
Track Construction	£20

Gordon Bennett Races

Coloured	£18
RP/Printed	£10

Isle of Man

Motor Cars/RP Close-up	£50
Action/RP Middle distance	£25

Valentine & Sons

Autocar Series	£8

Action/Portraits

Pre-1939	£15
1940 onwards	£7
Art Studies	£7

The Paris-Madrid race of May 1903 was an early experiment in auto racing .R/P £35

MOTOR CYCLE RACING

Isle of Man

Pre-1939	£25
1940 onwards	£12-£18

Racing/Other Circuits

Pre-1939	£18
1940 onwards	£10

Action/Portraits

Pre-1939	£18
1940 onwards	£8

MOUNTAINEERING

Everest	£10
Miscellaneous	£3

Early French motor racing, £12

OLYMPIC GAMES

Amongst the more collectable are those that capture real moments in sporting history whether it's Eric Liddell winning the 400 metres final in Paris (1924); Johnny Weissmuller at the Olympic pool in Paris (1924) or Amsterdam(1928); or Daley Thompson participating in Olympic Decathlon in the 1980s. Postcards of empty Olympic stadiums or poor photographs of competition in the distance will rarely draw the same interest.

SUMMER GAMES

1896 Athens	£10/£80
1900/04/08 Expos	£4/£25
1908 Competitors	£15-£20
1906 Athens	£3/£60
1912 Stockholm	£5/£30
1920 Antwerp	£8/£40
1924 Paris	£8/£30
1928/1956	£2/£15

1908 Olympics in London, Marathon winner J.J. Hayes from USA £15

1960/1968	£2/£7
1972/1988	£1/£7
1992/2012	£1/£2

WINTER GAMES

1924/1928	£10/£50
1932/1936	£3/£12
1948/1956	£3/£10
1960/1968	£2/£8
1972/1988	£1/£2
Ancient Olympia	£2
Empty Stadiums	£8/£12
Crowded Stadiums	£10/£20
Torch Ceremony	£2/£5

POLO
Miscellaneous	£3

ROWING
Named Crews	£6
Oxford Eights etc.	£6
Henley Regatta	£4

RUGBY FOOTBALL
International Teams	£20/£25
Rugby League professional teams	£15/£35
Rugby Union - major teams	£40
League/Union Teams	£30
Players/Named	£25
Amateur teams, local (both codes)	£6/£10
South African comic cards of internationals in UK 1907	£25

SAILING/YACHTING
Admiral's Cup	£5
Racing	£5
Kirk of Cowes/RP studies	£5
Powered Yachts	£5
General scenes	£3

SHOOTING
Scenes	£12
General Shooting	£5-£8

Rugby League, Wigan, £35

SKATING / RINKING
Miscellaneous	£3
Professional	£5

SPEEDWAY
Riders/Pre-1939	£18
Riders/Post-War	£12

SPORTS DAY/LOCAL SPORTS
Miscellaneous	£6

STADIA
British Football League	£45-£150
Overseas Football grounds	£5-£25
Amateur Grounds	£10-£20

Aston Villa's Stadium, No match in progress but still worth £45

Athletic Tracks UK	£15-£25
Athletic Tracks Overseas	£8

SWIMMING
Channel Swimming	£15-£25
Portraits of famous swimmers	£12
Miscellaneous	£6/12
Life Saving	£8/£20

TABLE TENNIS
Players/Competition	£25
Players/General	£8
Comic/Early	£25
Comic Sketches	£15

TENNIS
Wimbledon scenes (early)	£18
Wimbledon scenes	£12
Tournaments/Miscellaneous	£8/£15
Tennis Courts Amateur	£5
Comic Sketches	£7/£15

Players
Portraits/Chaplain Jones	£20
Portraits/E.A. Trim early period	£18
Portraits/E.A. Trim pre 1939	£15

*Tennis,
Early Trim
of
Wimbledon
Well
known
players*

£18

*Colour card showing Wembley Empire pool
with the London Lions Ice Hockey team   £4*

Competition/Pre-1939	£15
/1940 on	£8
Wimbledon series/c.1960	£5

WALKING

London-Brighton	£10
Other Races	£6
Comic	£3
Mountain Walking	£1

WATER POLO

Named Teams Photographic	£12
Miscellaneous	£8

WINTER SPORTS

Skating	£3
Skiing	£3
Climbing	£3
Tobogganing	£2
Art types	£4
Ice Hockey Teams Pre-1960	£20

WRESTLING/BODY BUILDING

Advertising poster type	£20-£25
Miscellaneous	£12/£20
Sandow	£15-£20
Hackenschmidt	£12-£15
Gymnasiums	£6-£12
Photographic Body Builders	£18

Mountain Climbing,   £3

*Hackenschmidt: This printed series will
sell for £12*

THEATRICAL

Part of the staple of the old publishers. Theatrical cards of all kinds filled the Edwardian albums, and have retained their popularity to the present day.

Market Report
There is an abundance of material which keeps prices low. This can be a very worthwhile hunting ground for the discriminating collector as there are some real bargains to be had.

ACTORS/ACTRESSES

Baker, Josephine	£60
Bernhardt, Sarah	£6
Coward, Noel	£15
Duncan, Isadora	£20
Hari, Mata	£30
Langtry, Lily	£8
Portraits/Miscellaneous	£1.50
Play Scenes	£1.50
Gaby Deslys	£3
Camille Clifford	£3

The predominant theme in this category is Edwardian Actors and Actresses of which vast quantities exist. Formerly little collected, they have now started to attract buyers, often looking for one or two named stars.
In the circumstances a price of £1.50 is considered reasonable for one card, but they can be picked up in bulk at auction, or from a dealer, at less than this figure.

Theatre advert, Edwardian actress £15

ADVERTISING

POSTER TYPE

Coloured	£15+
Black & White	£6

London Coliseum, part of a series of six showing this external view and 5 others of the interior, £6 each

Miscellaneous

Comedians/Performers	£5
Playbill Reproductions	£10
Play Scenes/With Advert	£3

Where applicable, the value of Poster Type cards is determined by the name of the Artist. See main Artist Index.

Ballet Dancer Adelina Genee £10

BALLET
Artistes

Fonteyn, Margot	£10
Genee, Dame Adelina	£10
Markova, Alicia	£10
Nijinsky	£60
Nureyev, R	£35
Pavlova	£12
Other Artists	£8
Companies/Troupes	£6
Post-war	£3

THEATRES

Music Hall/Variety	£25
Opera Houses	£4
Piers/Winter Gardens	£3
Interiors	£4
London West End/Coloured	£4

Prices for Theatres are for good, close-up mainly photographic studies and not for middle or far-distance views. Theatres forming part of a standard Street Scene are classed in that category.

Miners Theatre, Ashington   £12

Chirgwin, Music Hall performer, £8

Above: Theatre Poster advert £15

CIRCUS
ADVERTISING
Barnum & Bailey

Poster Type	£30
Others	£20

THE BRIDAL PARTY.   WEDDING OF TWO OF FRED ROPER'S MIDGETS.
GEORGE STODDART, 32 years old, 34 inches high.   EVA CRANE, 27 years old, 38 inches high.

Midgets   £8

Above:Variety artist / Female Body builder
£12

Buffalo Bill's Wild West

Poster Type	£25
Others	£20

Miscellaneous

Poster Types	£30
Others	£15

MISCELLANEOUS

Acts/Performers	£8-15
Animals Caged	£8
Bands	£8
Circus Sites/Identified G.B.	£40+

Clowns

Early/Chromo Litho	£20
Photographic Performers	£15

Freaks

Animal	£10
Human	£6-£15
Giants	£6-£15
Midgets/Troupes	£6-£12

VARIETY ARTISTS

Bard, Wilkie	£6
Chevalier, Albert	£6
Chirgwin	£8
Elliott, G.H.	£8
Forde, Florrie	£6
Formby, George	£12
King, Hetty	£6
Lauder, Harry	£6
/Comic	£6

Leno Dan	£6
Lloyd Marie	£8
Miller, Max	£10
Robey, George	£4
Stratton, Eugene	£8
Tate, Harry	£6
Tich, Little	£8
Tilley. `Vesta	£5

RADIO/TELEVISION

Children's Programmes/Radio	£6
Radio Celebrities	£4
Studios	£6
Transmitting Stations	£5
Wireless Sets	£8
QSL Cards/Radio Amateurs	£1
Comic Sketches	£6
Children's TV/Sooty etc.	£3
Brooke Bond Chimps	£3
Radio Pictorial Series	£5

MISCELLANEOUS

Amateur Dramatics	£1.50
Escapologists/Stuntmen	£20
Harry Houdini	£100+
Magicians/Conjurers	£25
Speciality Acts	£6
Ventriloquists	£25
Drag Artists	£4

JOSÉPHINE BAKER.
-Folies-Bergère-

101

Josephine Baker £60

Variety artist, Marie Lloyd £8

MARIE LLOYD

Autographs

Known Stars	£3+
Unknown Artists	£1

Prices quoted are for Autographs signed in ink. Printed Autographs have no value above that of the subject.(See page 210 for more details on Autographs)

Cabaret

French Skeletons	£1
Other Acts	£3

Concert Parties

Named Troupes	£4
Un-named	£1.50

Dancing

Ballroom/Stage etc.	£2
Greetings/Romance	£2

French Showgirls

`A Travers Les Coulisses'	£12
Moulin Rouge/Coloured	£12
Portraits/Miscellaneous	£3

TOPOGRAPHICAL

Turnpike Lane, R/P Top quality photographic, Well composed, lots to look at, Photo by Braddock £50

The most popular and eagerly sought after cards in the hobby, the finest of which have again seen a dramatic rise in price. Yet herein lies the enigma of Topographical cards, because it could be argued that the great majority of them are virtually unsaleable! As has often been said before, the problem with Topographical cards is that there are a great many very common cards of any particular area. These include the standard High Street views, local buildings of interest, the church and the park etc.; originally produced in vast quantities by regional and national publishers. And once the collector has obtained these common views he does not buy them again. They remain in the box, as any postcard dealer will testify, for possibly years! And being so common they keep turning up over and over again in the dealer's current buying. I would estimate that it would take an enthusiastic collector no more than six months to assemble a good collection of common cards such as these. But then he joins the rest of us in seeking the more elusive, and far more interesting back streets and scenes of local social history interest e.g. the Railway Station, Cinema, Theatre, Shop Fronts, Delivery Vehicles, Fairgrounds, Trams, Buses, Fires, Floods, Disasters, Post Offices, Public Houses, Windmills, Local Events etc. But these cards by their very nature were invariably produced in relatively small quantities by the local photographer, and today, some ninety years later, allowing for natural wastage, they are extremely thin on the ground. So as ever more collectors come to the hobby, all of them searching for these better cards, the prices go up and will continue to go up. It is an oft-repeated maxim in the postcard trade that you can sell cards like these but you cannot buy them! Indeed many of the really superb street scenes are now so highly saleable that they often don't get as far as the dealer's box or album, but are offered privately to the collector of that particular town at a negotiated price!

So this is the Topographical market we are at present faced with. There is nothing we can do about it, save to re-double our efforts to find the cards which collectors want.

If I may now look briefly at the production of Topographical cards and at the methods involved, the following notes may be of interest to collectors. These are based on a paper written by JHD Smith in conjunction with Brian Lund, which was published in 'Picture Postcard Monthly' in June 1982. They looked at the accepted definitions of 'Real Photographic' and 'Printed' cards, and suggested a more clearly defined structure, offering some thoughts toward a re-assessment of the Topographical nomenclature. To briefly summarise our conclusions, they were as follows:

Postcards were finished in two basical- ly different methods:

1. By a photographic process.
2. By a Printing Machine process.

PHOTOGRAPHIC
Local Photographers
By small, local firms producing each photograph individually, or in very small batches onto an existing post- card back, and hand-cutting or guillo- tining the batches, possibly four at a time. The style of finish varies widely, from the superb clarity of the very best examples, to the image which has almost faded away, according to the skill of the photographer in the devel-

Good quality, Sharp and bright images, produced by local firms using a photographic process £20

oping process. The caption was often hand-written, with the photographer's name or initials often appearing on the front of the card. These may be styled as the best examples of 'Real Photographic' cards, and the work of photographers such as Bragg, Gibson, Garratt, Wellsted, Ross, Braddock, Perkins and Daniell, immediately spring to mind as pre-eminent in this field. There are of course many other local photographers who produced superb work, and here there is a great deal of research yet to be done. These men concentrated upon their own immediate locality, and as a result it is in this work that you will find the fascinating cards of local history interest referred to above, and thus it follows that in these cards we are now see- ing the most significant advance in price.

Regional Publishers
Postcards were produced in quantity by larger companies who covered a wide circulation area. They probably used a mass-production technique involving contact printing from a neg- ative on to machines which could produce copies in large numbers. Many of these cards are designated 'Real Photographic' on the back, and are often found with a white border framing the picture. They are characterised by a uniform, glossy finish, the machine controlled output being less susceptible to variations in tone. Leading firms who worked in this style include Sankey, Camburn and E.T. Bush, covering the areas of Cumbria, S.E. England and South Wales respectively. The subjects depicted tend to be High Street and main street views, the Railway Station, Cinema, Theatre, Post Office, and other views of immediate local interest, although you will not find cards here, showing a line of barefoot children queueing up at a soup kitchen, this being essentially the province of the local man. Cards in this section do not gen- erally command such high prices, partly because they are more readily available, being pro- duced in larger quantities, and also because the scenes they depict tend to be more 'standard' than the off-beat work of the local photographer.

National Publishers
Also involved in postcard production, but this time on a national scale were big publishing houses such as Frith, Valentine, Davidson Bros, W.H.S. Kingsway Series and many others. Their work was machine produced and similar in all respects to that of the Regional Publishers both in style and content, but the difference lay in the fact that these were national publishing

PUBLISHED BY ~~E. J. & H. CLARKE~~ EAST FINCHLEY   No. 109

Printed postcard by local publisher £12

concerns who produced cards covering the length and breadth of the country. Prices here would fall into the same range as those for the Regional Publishers.

PRINTED CARDS

Without getting into a complex and perhaps misleading explanation of all the different printing techniques employed here, it is enough to state that if a card was not produced by one of the Photographic methods given above, in other words if it does not have a glossy finish, then it must have been produced by one of the many printing processes available at the time. Basically the method employed involved splitting the original photographic image into dots, or what is known as the screen process, and then transferring this on to a printing plate. While this method enabled mass produced copies of quite appalling definition to flood the market, the finest printed cards are the equal of the finest photographics. Here again we have three main areas of commerce.

Local Publishers
Many local photographers produced cards in a variety of printed formats, and some may have combined these with their own original photographic work. Many local shops and stores had their names overprinted on to the backs of cards produced for them by the Regional Publishers. The content of these cards, while being essentially local in character, does fall into the same style as that of the Regional Publishers above, and prices would be at approximately the same levels.

Regional Publishers
The work of Charles Martin in London and the South East perhaps most clearly illustrates the very high standard to which many Regional Publishers aspired. If we may include Lucien Levy also in this classification, some of his work is certainly the equal of anything in the entire Topographical field. Subjects depicted were again similar to those of the Regional Publishers of Photographic cards, the `line of hungry children' being always the work of what has been termed `the back-street photographer'. Prices for these cards fall into line with the other regional photographic work above.

National Publishers
Here we come to those cards which today form the great bulk of stock to be found in any dealer's box. Endless mass-produced stereotyped views by Frith, Judges, Valentine, Tuck, Stengel and many other substantial publishing corporations. Printed in a wide variety of styles, with many cards coloured, and nearly all of them depicting the standard views and tourist areas of any town or city, as well as incalculable numbers of Churches, Cathedrals, Seasides, Scottish Lochs and Welsh Mountains! Some, of course, are more interesting than others, but overall, these are the cards which the collector soon obtains. Prices for the majority of them are at the lower end of the price scale.

MARKET REPORT
There has been some resistance to rising price levels in this area. Many internet sellers are now adopting a set sale rather than auction driven approach on ebay which has resulted in less three figure prices being realized and because bargain hunters have bought cheaper than they would have at a traditional postcard fair. This is still the driving force of the hobby, and the entry point for most new collectors, but localized knowledge and rarity factors are all important.

Country Town R/P £15

London Suburb, R/P Animated scene £40

VILLAGES

Spectacular animated street scenes	£35+
Animated street scenes	£25
Other street scenes	£15
Empty streets	£6
Common Views/Landscapes	£2
Modern views/1945-1970	£3

COUNTRY TOWNS

Spectacular animated street scenes	£35+
Animated street scenes	£20
Other street scenes	£12-£15
Empty streets	£6
Common views/Town Hall etc.	£2
Modern views/1945-1970	£3

INDUSTRIALISED TOWNS AND CITIES

Spectacular animated street scenes	£30+
Animated street scenes	£20
Other street scenes	£12
Empty streets	£8
Common Views/City Centres etc.	£2
Modern views/1945-1970	£3

LONDON SUBURBAN

Spectacular animated street scenes	£40+
Animated street scenes	£25
Other street scenes	£15
Empty streets	£10
Common Views/Parks etc.	£3
Modern views/1945-1970	£3

LONDON CENTRAL

Spectacular animated street scenes	£25-£35
Animated street scenes	£15-£25
Other street scenes R/Photo	£10
Empty streets	£6
Oxford St./Regent St. etc.	£1.50
LL Published	£5-£12
Common Views/Trafalgar Square etc.	.50
Modern views/1945-1970	.50

London Central, R/P £20

Within these classifications many anomalies exist. For example, there are some superb animated LL cards of London Central, which at the same time are very common! With these, and similar examples, only knowledge and experience can be your guide. I have not tried to be too specific and break this down even further into considerations of `RP, Printed, Coloured, Local and National

Hatfield street scene Pr. £15

TOPOGRAPHICAL

Photographers etc., as this would only lead to confusion. I have not even tried to separate Real Photographic from Printed cards because, as we all know, there are some awful RPs, and some very fine Printed types. I have, however, given the main category to those superb Topographical views of both kinds which stand out in any collection.

* Animated Street Scenes: A card which is full of activity, life and movement, or which depicts a scene of particular relevance to that area, or is otherwise of unusual interest. These cards are very much the exception, often being produced by the local photographer. The majority of street scenes in any dealer's stock would be classified as `Other street scenes'.

Local published, Multi-view card £4

MISCELLANEOUS

Abbeys/Convents/Priories	£1.50
Aerial Views	£5
Archaeological Sites/Villages	£1.50
Bridges/Viaducts	£4
Castles	£1.50
Cathedrals	£1
Chapels	£3
Churches	£2
Crystal Palace	£3
Follies	£5
Greetings/Town Names	£1.50
Holiday areas	£1
Hotels	£6
Interiors	£1.50
Lake District scenery	£1
Landscapes	£1
Manor Houses	£5
Monuments/Memorials	£3
Multi-view	£4
Municipal Buildings	£3
Parks	£3
Seaside/Common views	.50
Special Events	£20
Stately Homes	£1.50
Much photographed buildings	£1

Essex, Printed £6

Huddersfield, R/P Larger towns £7

Every dealer will have his own idea of the value of any card backed up by a specialised knowledge of his own area, so at best, the prices above should only be taken as a broad general average, capable of movement up or down as determined by the particular card.

Maidstone, Kent, Colour photo £8

London Suburb, Early R/P £12

Bracknell, Shops and street Sc. R/P £22

Post Office Printed £15

Winchester, R/P £28

High Street, Turriff, Scotland Photo £18

Stonebridge, R/P street scene £30

Pub, Crown Inn, Chiddingfold, R/P £16

London, Brixton, animated £25

SOCIAL HISTORY: BEHIND THE SHOP FRONT

"COACH and HORSES," Stonebridge Park, Willesden, N.W.
Proprietor .... *W. T. ECCLESTONE (Jolly Jumbo).*
Height—5 ft. 9½ ins. Stomach—6ft. 1½ ins. Chest—5ft. Thigh—30½ ins.
Calf—23½ ins. Arm—22 ins. Foot—9½ ins. long. Weight—38 st., former
Weight—38 st.

Left: Pub Landlord £15, Above: Close up Baker shop front £35

Pub Interior, £25

Shop Front Printed advert £20

Shop front, Real photo, Street scene £18

SOCIAL HISTORY

This is Topographical by another name and the same comments apply. You can almost name your own price for the better RP studies and the scarce cards of local history interest. At the same time there are a great many interesting cards in this classification which are very reasonably priced.

It is pointed out that for all relevant entries e.g. Fairs . Post Offices . Public Houses .

Street Markets . Windmills etc. the stated priceis a broad average figure for a card, either RP or Printed, fully identified and showing a 'Close-up at a named location', with Real Photographic cards being the most desirable. Unlocated cards and middle or far-distance views would be priced accordingly.

Please see WHAT THE PRICES MEAN on P.30 ***

AGRICULTURE

Agricultural Shows	£15
Carting	£12
Crofters	£6
Dalesmen	£5
Farm Machinery/Tractors etc	£18
Farms	£8
Farmworkers	£6
Flower Picking	£6
Fruit Picking	£6
Herdsmen	£5
Trees	£1.50

Harvesting

Reaping	£5
Threshing machines/Located	£35
/Unlocated	£20
Hay Carts/RP studies	£8
General Harvesting scenes	£3

Hop Picking

Demonstrations in Kent	£75
Real Photographic scenes/Located	£20
/Unlocated	£10

There are many superb RP studies of Hop Picking. Everything depends upon location.

Cooper's Series/Maidstone/RP	£15

The "Kent" Series/Invicta

Pub: G.A. Cooper/A.N. Hambrook	£8
Young & Cooper/Bw	£8
/Coloured	£4

There are certain Y&C coloured cards which are very common.

Filmer's Home Hop Picking Series	£8
T.A. Flemons/Tonbridge	£8
"Solochrome" Series/E.A. Sweetman	£6
"Solograph" Series/E.A. Sweetman	£6

For Hampshire/Worcestershire etc. follow the price guide above.

Foreign Hop Picking	£5

Lavender Industry

Fields/Growing	£8
Picking	£10
Carting	£35

Ploughing

Oxen in Sussex/RP	£25
/Printed	£8
Plough Horses	£3
Ploughing/General scenes	£2

Sheep

Lambing	£6
Shearing	£12
Sheep Dips	£12
Sheepdog Trials	£12
Shepherds	£6
/South Downs/RP studies	£10

CANALS

Aqueducts/Bridges/Locks	£8
Barges/Close-up	£40
Canal construction/Workers	£40
Disasters	£40
Events/Gatherings, etc.	£40
Military Canals	£3
Tunnels	£8

Modern Canal scene R/P £3

Narrow Canals
Spectacular Real Photographic	£50
Real Photographic	£10/£15
Coloured/Sepia/BW	£6
Common views/Hythe, Llangollen etc.	£2

Ship Canals
Caledonian/Crinan/Exeter etc.	£2
Manchester Ship Canal	£5

River Navigations
Traffic/Close-up	£15
General views	£6

As with other Subjects, a particularly good card or an unusual view on a seldom photographed Canal, would fetch a price well in excess of these general figures.

COAL MINING
Coal Miners
Groups/Portraits	£20/£30

Collieries
Surface/Close-up	£20/£40
/Middle Distance	£12
Somerset Coalfield	£25
Underground	£10
Models	£6
Pit Girls	£10
Open-cast Mining	£30
Art Type	£2
Coal Picking	£60

Certain views of Collieries in South Wales, published by M.J.R.B. have been remaindered and are therefore worth considerably less than the prices given above.

Series
Kinsley Evictions 1905	£50

For full details on this series please refer to PPV 2003
M. Brookes/Pontypridd	£10
Cannock Chase	£10
Clay Cross Co./Set 25	£10

Ashford Cycle club £15

Timothy's Series/South Wales	£10
Other series	£10

A number of Collieries produced series of cards depicting work both at the surface and underground.

Disasters
Hamstead Colliery	£15
Senghenydd Colliery	£30
Other Named Events	£25
In Memoriam Cards	£25
In Memoriam Gothard	£20/£75
Rescue Teams	£20

CRIME & PUNISHMENT
Judges/Barristers	£6
Prisons	£5
Prisoners at Work	£5
Warders at Dartmoor	£1.50
Prisoners at Portland	£1.50

CYCLING
Close-up RP studies	£6
Cycle clubs Named location	£15-£20
Tandems	£10
Tricycles	£15
Military	£5
Greetings/Romantic	£3
Comic Sketches	£3

Advert Cards
Poster Type	£40
Others	£15

See also SPORT

DISASTERS
Coast Erosion/Landslips	£15
/Black Rock/Brighton	£2
Explosions	£20
Floods	£20
Frozen Seas	£6
In Memoriam Cards	£20
Lightning Damage	£18
Snow Damage	£15
Storm Damage	£18
Subsidence	£20
Wrecked Buildings/Piers	£15
War Damage/WW1 Air Raids	
/Ramsgate	£12
/Scarborough	£8
Other locations	£15

Earthquakes
Essex 1884	£8
Other locations/GB	£20
Messina	£1.50
San Francisco	£5
Other locations/Foreign	£3

Events

Faversham 1916/Funeral scenes	£15
Lincoln Typhoid Outbreak 1905	£60
Louth Floods 1920	£18
Lynmouth Floods 1952	£8
Newport Dock 1909	£50
Northwich Subsidence	£12
Norwich Floods	£12
Southend Pier	£10
Vanguard Motor Accident/ Handcross 1906	£10
Weston Super Mare Storm 1903	£12
Worthing Pier	£10

DOMESTIC LIFE
Corkscrews	£8
Knitting	£4
Weddings/Brides/Groups	£2
/Wedding Cakes	£2

Country Houses
Buildings	£4
Domestic Servants	£5
Gardens	£2
Kitchens	£5

Photography
Cameras/Equipment	£8
Greetings/Romantic	£4
Comic Sketches	£6
Stereoscopic cards	£4

These are cards with two adjacent pictures, best viewed through a Stereo viewer for full effect.
There are many different series and subjects.

Telephones
Correspondence cards	£8
Telephone in photograph	£4
Telephone Exchanges/Operators	£20
Greetings/Romantic	£3
Comic Sketches	£2

FAIRS
Amusement Parks	£5
Southend Kursaal	£5
Wall of Death/Action photos	£18
/Arenas	£8
Fetes	£12
Seaside Fairs/Water Chutes	£5

Feats/Wagers
Walking Round the World	£12
/George M. Schilling	£7
/Man in the Iron Mask	£8
Niagara Falls Barrel	£8
Other Stunts	£10+

Markets
Animal Markets	£15
Street Markets	£15

See note on pricing at beginning of section.

London Markets
Club Row	£8
Farringdon Road	£5
Petticoat Lane	£5
Billingsgate Market	£8
Smithfield Market	£8
Woolwich	£5

Travelling Fairs
Barnet Horse Fair	£22
Cosham Fair	£25
Hampstead Heath/A&G Taylor	£60
/Star Series	£5
Hull Fair	£20
Mitcham Fair	£25
Nottingham Goose Fair	£10
Oxford Fair	£15
Other named locations	£25
Fairground Equipment	£20+
RP studies/Published c.1950	£5

See note on pricing at beginning of section. There are in circulation many privately produced, postcard-size plain back photographs of Fairground equipment. Most of these have been printed in quantity from an existing negative and consequently have only a nominal value.

Fire Brigade Station & Horse Drawn. R/P £30

FIRE BRIGADE
Firemen	£15
Fire fighting/Identified	£15
/Unidentified	£6
Fire Stations	£20-£30
Tuck Oilettes	£8

Fire Engines
Hand Drawn	£40
Horse Drawn	£40
Motor	£40

Fires
Bon Marche/Brixton	£5

Lewes	£6
Selby Abbey	£3
Other GB Fires	£12+
Art Sketches	£3

FISHING INDUSTRY
Deep Sea Fishing
Fish sales on quayside Real photo	£15-40
Fish sales on quayside	£15
Fish Markets	£3-£8
General quayside scenes	£3-£8
Herring Girls	
/Gutting/Packing Herring	£6
/Spectacular RP studies	£15
Fishermen	£3
Mending Nets	£3
Fishwives at Newhaven etc.	£1
French scenes/Concarneau etc.	£3
Other French scenes	£2
Foreign scenes	£1.50

It is pointed out that in the 'Fish Markets' classification there are a number of very common cards, worth about £1.50 each, which are always turning up. Unfortunately it is not possible to list these individually without showing illustrations, but you have been warned.

Trawlers/Drifters
RP Trawler studies	£12
General studies	£6
/c.1960 RP studies	£1.50
On board Trawler	£12
Trawler fleet at sea	£3

Tuck Oilette Series
2317	Toilers of the Sea	£4
2761	Toilers of the Sea	£4
2817	Toilers of the Sea	£4
6690	Toilers of the Deep	£4

Local Industry
Keddle Net Fishing/Rye	£25
Prawn Fishermen/Bognor	£15
Coracle Fishermen	£5
Cockle Gatherers	£15
Cockle Vendors	£15

GIPSIES
Camps
GB locations	£25-£35
/Unlocated	£15
Alien Immigrants/Pub. Hartmann	£10
Macedonian Gipsies at Epping	£15

On the Road
GB locations	£35
/Unlocated	£12

Gipsy Encampment £25

HUNTING
Tuck Oilette Series
2732	Fox and Stag Hunting	£4
2758	Hunting	£4
3596	Hunting in the Shires	£4
9801	In the Hunting Field	£4

Miscellaneous
Photographic groups/Named Hunts	£6
/Un-named Hunts	£3
Other photographic studies	£3
The Owl Series	£1.50
Comic Sketches	£2
Art Studies	£3

Industrial, Mining, R/PNo location hence £12

INDUSTRIAL
Delabole Slate Quarry	£5
Gas Works	£15
Greenwich Telescope	£2
Power Houses	£6
Printing Works	£6
/Evening News	£8
Royal Mint/Two sets of 12 cards	
Price per set	£1.50
Saltworks	£25
Science Museum Series	£3
Steelworks	£12

Cotton Mills		
Interior/Machines	£8	
Exterior views	£8	
Lancashire Weaving scenes	£8	

Factories

Interior/Machines	£8	
Exterior views	£8	
Machine Shops	£6	
Men at work	£6	
Cammell Laird/20 cards		
Industrial sketches	£6	
Vickers of Barrow/Production scenes		
RP series/Valentine	£8	
Woolwich Arsenal WHS Series	£6	

Pottery Industry

Factory Scenes	£6	
Exteriors/Kilns etc.	£12	
Craft Pottery/Throwing etc.	£10	
Poole Pottery/14 cards	£3	
Worcester Royal Porcelain Co. Ltd/		
Set 6/Tuck Oilette	£1.50	

Tin Mining/Cornish Mines

RP/Close-up view	£25	
/Middle distance	£15	
Printed views	£10	
Refining/Dressing processes/RP	£40	

The great majority of Tin Mining cards were produced as Real Photographs by local photographers such as Bragg, Govier and Caddy etc.

MEDICAL

Asylums	£5	
Operations/Surgical	£8	
Ward Scenes	£6	

St John Ambulance R/P Named location £15

Cottage Hospitals	£5
Hospitals	£5
Nurses	£3
Red Cross	£5
St. John's Ambulance Brigade	£5+

Ambulances

Horse-Drawn	£35
Motor	£25

Dentistry

Surgeries	£15
Comic Sketches	£12

Medical, Hospital ward scene £6

POLICE

Policemen/RP portraits	£6
Police Stations	£12
Special Constabulary/RP portraits	£5
Comic Sketches	£3
Art Studies	£4

POSTAL

Royal Mail Vans	£35
Hand Carts/Traps	£35
Pillar Boxes	£5
Romantic/Greetings	£3
Comic Telegrams	£3
Comic Sketches	£3

Mail Coaches

At named locations/G.B.	£25
Art Type	£5

POSTMEN

RP Studies	£12
Art Studies	£5
Comic Sketches	£4

Postmen of the World/Set 48

Kunzli Freres	£10

Postmen of the British Empire/Set 14

Colman's Starch	£10

POST OFFICES

Sorting Offices	£20
Villages	£20
Towns	
Main Office	£15
Sub Post Office	£25
Cities	
Main Offices	£8
Sub Post Office	£25

See note on pricing at beginning of section.

Delivery Vehicles/Staff Groups
Posed outside building	£50

Fundraising and a shop front R/P   £20

RELIGION
ANGLICAN CHURCH
Bishops	£1.50
Clergy named	£1.50
Events/Processions	£5

Evangelism

Missionary depot of Liverpool, Advertising for people to spread the word in Japan £15

Caravans	£25
Church Army	£3
Conventions/Meetings	£6
Gipsy Smith	£3
Personalities	£3
Wesleyan Churches	£3

Oberammergau
Actors/Portraits	£1
Production scenes/Views	£1

ROMAN CATHOLICISM
Cardinals/Bishops	£1.50
Priests named	£1.50
Events/Processions etc.	£2
Lourdes scenes	£1

Popes
Coronation Souvenir Cards	£5
Jubilee Cards	£5
Mourning Cards/Leo XIII	£5
Funeral Processions	£3

Portraits	£2

MISCELLANEOUS
Angels/Saints etc.	£4
Lord's Prayer	£1.50
Mission Societies	£3
Missionaries	£3
/In the Pot	£3
Monks/Local Industry	£2

For Churches and Religious buildings see TOPOGRAPHICAL

RETAIL TRADE
Delivery Vehicles
Hand Carts	£35
Horse-drawn Carts	£40
Milk Floats	£50
Motor Vehicles	£30

See also MOTOR TRANSPORT

Public Houses
Delivery Vehicles/Staff Groups
posed outside building	£50
Close-up view	£25
Pub in street scene	£10

See note on pricing at beginning of section. A pub in a street scene would be priced as a Topographical card. It must also be borne in mind that there are many very common pubs to be found on postcards. For example: The Star/Alfriston, Bull and Bush/Hampstead, Cat and Fiddle/New Forest, Jerusalem Inn/Nottingham and many others too numerous to list. These are worth much less than the quoted prices and only through experience will you learn which ones they are.

Breweries
Guinness Brewery Scenes	£8
6x4 size	£6
Local Breweries	£35

Shop Fronts
Delivery Vehicles/Staff Groups
posed outside building	£50

Shop front R/P located £20

Special Displays/Meat Hanging etc.	£40
Grocer/Tobacconist/Newsagent etc.	
Spectacular Close-up RP/Located	£35
/Unlocated	£15
Other displays/Located	£20
/Unlocated	£5
Picture Postcard Displays	£50
Arcades	£10
Rationing queues	£40
Station Bookstalls/W.H.S. etc.	£20

See note on pricing at beginning of section. There are far more unlocated Shop Fronts than those which can clearly be assigned to a particular town or village.

RURAL LIFE

Allendale Wolf	£5
Barrel Organs/Men	£60
Blacksmiths	£18
Bootmakers	£25
Brusher Mills	£5
Children's Games	£5
Chimney Sweeps	£25
Cliff Climbers	£8
Coopers	£18
Cornish Pasties	£2
Deer Stalking	£3
Flower Shows	£8
Hermits	£12
Hunting/Shooting	£3
Milkmaids	£3
Odd Characters	£12
Open Air Gatherings	£5
Ox Roasts/Pig Roasts	£25
Pea Picking	£5
Peat Digging	£6
Seaweed Gathering/Wracking	£3
Spinning/Weaving	£4
Irish Spinning Wheels	£1.50
Street Furniture/Troughs	£6
Street Parades/Processions	£15

Price is governed by the subject and location.

Tobacco Auctions/USA	£6
Trug Making	£40
Village Crafts	£3
Village Folk	£2
Village Life	£3

There are a number of Tuck Oilette series on this theme, which would carry the price of the respective Artist.

Water Carts	£30
Watercress Growing	£20
Wheelwrights	£30
Workers in the fields	£5

Charcoal Burning

Actual work in progress/RP	£25
Huts/Forest clearings etc.	£5

Folklore

Banbury Cross	£1.50
County Humour/Dialect	£1.50
Customs & Traditions	£1.50
Dunmow Flitch	£8
Ducking Stools/Stocks	£1.50
Epitaphs	£1.50
Ghosts	£2
Gretna Green	£1
Lady Godiva	£5

There are many cards of different personalities playing this part.

Legends	£1.50
Maypole Celebrations/Located	£18
/Unlocated	£5
Morris Dancers	£15
Well Dressing	£6
Witches	£5

Funerals

Celebrities	£18
Special Events/Processions	£12
Other Funerals	£6

Lacemaking

GB locations/Named Lacemakers	£25
Industrial/Factory scenes	£6
Belgium	£4

Village Pageant rural scene £8

| France | £8 |
| Other Foreign | £5 |

Performing Bears

GB locations	£100
/Unlocated	£30
Foreign	£12

Refuse Collection

| Dustcarts | £40 |

SCHOOLS

Universities/Colleges	£2
Public Schools/Eton etc.	£2
Grammar/Secondary	£6
Village Schools	£8
Classroom groups/Identified	£8
/Unidentified	£1.50

SEASIDE

Donkeys	£3
Bathing Machines	£5
Pierrot/Beach Shows	£5
Piers	£3+
Punch & Judy	£12
Sand Models	£3
Seaside Amusements	£8

Beach Scenes

| Animated RP | £10 |
| General scenes | £1.50 |

HOLIDAY CAMPS

Butlins

| Pre-1960 | £4/£8 |
| 1961 onwards | £3 |

Butlins produced cards with inset pix of their respective Holiday Camps.

Pontins/Warners etc.

| Pre 1960 | £3 |
| 1961 onwards | £1.50 |

Local Camps/Holiday Villages

| Pre 1960 | £3-£8 |

Seaside Amusements £8

| 1961 onwards | £1.50 |
| Caravan Parks | £3 |

There exist many modern 6x4 size cards of Holiday Camps which would be worth less than the prices quoted above.

WATERMILLS

Scarce types	£18
Middle range	£5
Common types	£2
Fires/Disasters	£25
Art types	£1
Foreign	£1.50

WINDMILLS

Scarce types	£35
Middle range	£15
Common types	£3
Fires/Disasters	£35
Art types	£1.50
Foreign	£3

See note on pricing at beginning of section. With both Watermills and Windmills it is difficult to be more specific, without listing and illustrating every card. In both cases there are some very common cards which are always turning up. With Watermills, those at Laxey, Groudle Glen and Guy's Cliff are familiar to all collectors,while in Windmills, Salvington, Rottingdean and Wimbledon are virtually unsaleable. Beyond these, there is a broad band of middle range cards, which although relatively common, are usually saleable if priced realistically. At the top of the range are cards which are seldom found, and where only a few copies may exist.
Also with Windmills there are many post-1945 cards which would carry half the prices.quoted above.
Only knowledge and experience can be your guide.

WELFARE ORGANISATIONS

Workhouses	£12
N.S.P.C.C.	£12
Y.M.C.A./Y.W.C.A.	£3
John Grooms's Crippleage	£1.50
Lord Mayor Treloar Home	£1.50
Newcastle-upon-Tyne Street Life/	
Pub. Thompson & Lee	£15
Waifs and Strays	£3
Childrens' Homes	£6
Orphanages	£5

Charities/Fund Raising

Flag Days	£15
Fund Raising Animals	£12
T.B. Fund Raising	£8

See also MILITARY/WW1

Dr. Barnardo

Portraits	£3
Funeral Procession at Barkingside	£20
Homes	£3
Children at Work	£3
Children in group photos	£3
'Our Young Migrants in Canada'	£12

This was a scheme now discredited where Barnardos sent children to the Colonies. Believed to be two sets of 6 cards.

Salvation Army

Bands	£6
Gen. Booth/Visits G.B.	£20
Gen. Booth/Memorial Card	£8
Gen. Booth/Portraits	£3/£12
Miscellaneous interest	£3

YOUTH ORGANISATIONS
SCOUTING
Baden Powell

Tuck Empire Series	£25
Early Vignettes/Coloured	£25
/b.w.	£12
Relief of Mafeking	£30
Portraits	£12
Visits	£20

Portraits/Groups

Tuck R. & Sons/Payne H	£25
Other Series	£10

Camps/Located	£10
/Unlocated	£5
Scouts/Troops Identified	£10
/Unidentified	£2
Comic Sketches	£12

National Series

Published by Millar & Lang in sets of 6 cards.
Prices are for individual cards.

Series 749	£10
Series 760	£10
Series 845	£10
Series 858	£10
Series 919	£10
Series 1000	£10
Series 1002	£10
Series 1044	£10
Series 1572	£10
Price per set of those listed above	£75
Other Millar & Lang issues	£8

Personalities

Jack Cornwell V.C.	£10

Miscellaneous

H.Q. Official Cards	£15
Jamborees	£15

A special postmark on these cards adds to their value.

Tuck R. & Sons/Our Boy Scouts/ Oilette Series 9950/Animal Heads W.H. Ellam	£100
Price per set	£750
Scouts of the World/Set 111 USA 1968/Price for complete set	£75

GIRL GUIDES
Leaders

Lady Baden Powell	£10
Princess Mary	£5
Princess Elizabeth	£5
Other Leaders	£5

Portraits/Groups

Official Cards	£5
Identified	£5
Unidentified	£1.50

MISCELLANEOUS

Boys Brigade	£10
Church Lads Brigade	£6
Other Organisations	£3

2nd NORTH LONDON TROOP. 1913.

Scouting , Troop published card £15

LONDON LIFE
and other Social History Series

Many Edwardian postcard firms published series of cards reflecting the Life and Labour of those times, while other companies produced long series covering Events and Disasters. These cards today are highly prized, and in many cases form a unique historical record of social conditions. The value of the Picture Postcard as a contemporary reference can be clearly seen in many of the examples listed below.

Market Report
Little movement in this market except for the top quality Real Photo social scenes. Popular among some established dealers who have advanced collections and have given up looking for the gaps. The issues starting below are good quality numbered series worth collecting.

ARISTOPHOT
391 Flower Girls	£10
392 Omnibus	£25
395 Policeman	£10
398 Omnibuses in a row	£15
401 Feeding Pigeons	£15
404 District Messenger boy	£12
411 Dust Cart	£18
412 The Coal man	£20
413 Street Vendors	£15
414 Hansom Cab	£20
415 Sandwich Types	£10
417 Boot Cleaner	£12
418 Fine Ripe Cherries	£10
419 London Beer	£20

London Types. The Coal Man. &Ea.412.

ARISTOPHOT,No.412, The Coal Man,

BEAGLES J. & CO.
001 The Costermonger	£18
002 The Policeman	£18
003 The Shoe Black	£12
004 The German Band	£12
005 The Parcel Post	£20
006 The Flower Sellers	£10
006 The Horse Omnibus	£18
007 A Newsvendor	£15
008 The Flower Sellers	£10
008 The Street Organ	£15
010 The Knife Grinder	£15
011 Drinking Fountain & Cattle Trough	£10

013 The Pavement Artist	£12
014 The Paper Boy	£12
015 The Telegraph Messenger	£12
016 The Electric Tram	£40
018 The Milkman	£18
018 The Flower Sellers	£10
019 The Baker	£15
020 The Postman	£15
022 The Chelsea Pensioner	£10
411 Dust Cart	£20
646K A London Policeman	£12
647N Policeman holding up the traffic	£12
648E City of London Ambulance	£18

W. HAGELBERG
Series 3490
Thames Embankment	£8
Coffee & Cocoa Stall	£8
Middlesex Street/Old Petticoat Lane	£8

JOHN WALKER
22607 Street Music	£25
22671 Petticoat Lane	£15
22672 Petticoat Lane	£15
22691 Bank Holiday	£30

LL/LOUIS LEVY
London Types
301 Beefeater at the Tower of London	£8
302 Pavement Artist	£8
303 The Fireman	£12
325 Policeman	£8

G. SMITH
Types of London Life
01 Pavement Artist	£8
04 Flower Seller at Piccadilly Circus	£12
05 Newsboy	£12
05a A Newsboy	£12
06 Shoe Black at Trafalgar Square	£12
07	
08 The Fireman	£12
09 A Bus Driver	£15
10 Police Ambulance	£15
11 Policeman holding up Traffic at theBank	£12

12 Postman	£12
13 Messenger Boy	£12
14 Street Sweeper	£15
15 Fruit Seller	£15
16 Hot Chestnut Man	£15
17 The Lord Mayor's Coachman	£12
18 Punch & Judy Show at National Portrait Gallery	£15
19 A Horse Bus	£15
20 A Messenger Boy	£12
21	
22 Sentry at Buckingham Palace	£8

Research by Philip Richards who informs me that although this is the main series of Gordon Smith "Types of London Life", there are certain titles known in another un-numbered series, as well as other cards in the style within the publisher's general range.

Types of London Life (16): Hot Chestnut Man.

G.SMITH,
No.16
Hot
Chestnut
Man £15

LONDON LIFE.- No.16. THE ELECTRIC TRAM. BEAGLES POSTCARDS.
THE TRAMS ARE OF THE GREATEST CONVENIENCE TO THE THOUSANDS OF PERSONS TRAVELLING IN LONDON, PARTICULARLY TO CONVEY THE WORKERS TO AND FROM THE CITY.
BELOW THE CAR IS A SAFETY DEVICE TO PREVENT ANY PERSON FROM BEING RUN OVER, SHOULD THEY ACCIDENTALLY BE KNOCKED DOWN IN FRONT OF THE CAR.

*Above: **BEAGLES 'THE ELECTRIC TRAM'** Number 16. Superb Photo £40*

PHOTOCROM CO.
Celesque Series/Coloured London Types

Covent Garden Porter	£6
Shoe Black	£10
Flower Seller	£6
The Smithfield Market Porter	£6
The Bus Conductor	£10
The Pavement Artist	£6
The Recruiting Sergeant	£6
The Street Hawker	£10
The Newsboy	£6
The Life Guard	£6
The Orderly Boy	£10
The Postman	£10
The Chelsea Pensioner	£6
The Lighterman	£10

CHARLES SKILTON
Set of 12 cards c.1940	£18

TUCK R. & SONS
A10 A Policeman	£12
A11 The Recruiting Sergeant	£12
A12 A Fruit Hawker	£18
A13 Flower Vendors	£12
A14 A Messenger Boy	£12
A15 A Shoeblack	£18
A16 A Pavement Newsvendor	£12
A17 A Sandwichman & Newsvendor	£18
A18 A Cabman on the Rank	£18
A19 A Policeman controlling Traffic	£12
A20 A Pavement Hawker	£18
A21 A Pavement Artist	£12

WYNDHAM SERIES
6335 Hawking Butcher	£30
7579 Fish Stall	£30
7587 Mending Door Mats	£30
7588 Penny Scales	£30
7589 Salt & General Merchant	£30
7590 Sweep snow away	£30
7591 The Potman	£30
7592 Shrimps	£30
7593 Mixed Quartette	£30
7594 Caravan Carpenter	£30
7595 Hot Potatoes	£30

7596 Fruit Merchant	£30
7597 Pussy's Butcher	£30
7598 Sweeps	£30
7599 Muffins	£30
7600 Toy Vendor	£30
7601 Old Clo	£30
7602 Dustman	£30
7603 Shoeblack	£30
7604 Shoeblack	£30
7605 Street Musician	£30
7606 Whelks	£30
7607 Laces	£30

STAR SERIES
Set of 36 cards

01 Good Old Hampstead. The Cockney's Paradise
02 Milk Fresh from Tin Cow at St. James' Park.
03 The Nurse's Paradise, Hyde Park.
04 Feeding the Ducks in a London Park
05 Feeding the Pigeons in a London Park
06 The Fountains. Trafalgar Square.
07 Sweep O.
08 O.H.M.S.
09 The Little Bird will tell your Fortune for one Penny
10 Shoeblack and Cabby.
11 Fireman and Escape.
12 On Guard. Buckingham Palace.
13 Recruiting Sergeant and a Policeman. "On Point Duty".
14 Aliens.
15 Harmony.
16 A free Drink for Man's Best Friend.
17 Fine Fruit and Fresh Flowers. Farringdon Market, Farringdon Street.
18 Covent Garden.
19 All a Blowing and a Growing.
20 A Hot Day. Give us a Taster Jack.
21 Kerbstone Merchants. "Wonderful Pennorths". Ludgate Hill.
22 Paper Kiosk outside the "Prudential" Holborn. A well-known Landmark.
23 Regent Circus. "Fresh from Market".
24 The Busy Bargees. River Thames.
25 Off to a Fire.
26 Changing the guard. Horseguards.
27 Fatigue Duty. Buckingham Palace Road.
28 Motor Bus.
29 Electric Tram and "2d" Tube Station.
30 A Free Drink in a London Park.
31 London Bridge
32 Piccadilly Circus
33 Rotten Row. Hyde Park.
34 Mansion House and Cheapside.
35 G.P.O. and St. Martin's le Grand.
36 Holborn Viaduct and City Temple.

Price Range: £3/£6. (The printing technique of this series leaves much to be desired).

LONDON LIFE. - No. 7. A NEWSVENDOR. BEAGLES' POSTCARDS.
N MANY FAVOURABLE SPOTS FOR CUSTOM. NEWSVENDORS HAVE SECURED AN ODD CORNER OR RAILING, WHICH SERVES IN PLACE OF SHOP FOR THE SALE OF THEIR WIDE SELECTION OF PERIODICALS AND NEWSPAPERS

BEAGLES, *No.7, The Newsvendor* £15

ROTARY PHOTOGRAPHIC CO.
London Life/Series 10513

01 Fireman	£25	21 District Messenger Boy	£25
02 Postman	£25	22 Big Bens Telescopeman	£25
03 Street Orderly Boy	£25	23 Post Office Telegraph Boy	£30
04 Taxi-Cab Driver	£25	24 LCC Tramcar Conductor	£35
05 Newspaper Boy	£25	25 Reuter Telegraph Co.'s Messenger	£20
06 Pavement Artist	£20	26 The Milkman	£35
07 Hot Chestnut Seller	£35	27 The Baked Potato Man	£35
08 Lifeguardsman Sentry	£20	28 A Woman Pavement Artist	£25
09 Toy Seller	£25	29 City Police Motor Ambulance	£30
10 "Votes for Women"	£75	30 "Votes for Women"	£65
11 District Messenger	£25	31 Billingsgate Porter	£25
12 Flower Seller	£25	32 Smithfield Market Porter	£35
13 Omnibus Driver	£35	33 Covent Garden Porters	£35
14 Hansom "Cabby"	£35	34 Chelsea Pensioner	£25
15 Bootblack	£30	35 Firemen at Work	£20
16 Hawker	£25	36 Street Fruit Hawker/ Coster Barrow	£35
17 City Police Constable	£25	37 Street Orderly Man	£35
18 Flower Sellers	£20	38 Boy Scouts	£35
19 Fortune Teller	£25	39 Chimney Sweep	£25
20 The Brewers Man	£35	40 Sandwich Board Man	£35

10513—74   LONDON LIFE   THE DUSTMAN.   ROTARY PHOTO. E.C.

ROTARY, No. 74 The Dustman   £45

ROTARY PHOTOGRAPHIC CO.
London Life/Series 10513 (contd.)

41 Automatic Road Sweeper	£35
42 Royal Exchange Constable	£25
43 Newspaper Boys with latest news	£30
44 Ice Cream	£35
45 An Apple Woman	£25
46 Recruiting Sergeants	£20
47 Coster in his Donkey Cart at Covent Garden Market	£35
48 Flower Sellers at Oxford Circus	£35
49 Underground Tube Train Conductor	£45
50 Boulters Lock on Ascot Sunday	£35
51 A Scene at Henley during Regatta Week	£35
52 A Racecourse Scene at Epsom	£35
53 The King is Coming	£35
54 Opera enthusiasts. Queue outside Covent Garden Opera House	£35
55 A Night Watchman	£35
56 A Coffee Stall Supper, "Al Fresco"	£45
57 A Whelk Stall	£35
58 A Motor Bus. One of London's Red Generals	£45
59 Postman collecting the Midnight Post	£35
60 Fireman at work at a midnight Fire	£30
61 An Underground Railway Lift Man	£45
62 GPO Royal Mail Motor	£35
63 Knives and Scissors Grinder	£35
64 A Baker's Man	£35
65 A Flower Seller	£35
66 A Coal Man	£40
67 A Butcher	£35
68 A Hospital Nurse	£45
69 Early Morning in Rotten Row, Hyde Park	£25
70 Football. Chelsea V Aston Villa at Stamford Bridge	£180
71 Arrest of a Militant Suffragette	£85
72 Rushing to a Fire at Night	£30
73 Steam Roller at work	£55
74 The Dustman	£45
75 A helpful member of our Dumb Friends League	£35
76 A Boy Scout's Band	£45
77 "Four Wheeler" Cab	£45
78 A City Window Cleaner	£35
79 Turkish Baths Advertiser	£35

10513—73   LONDON LIFE. STEAM-ROLLER AT WORK.   ROTARY PHOTO, E C.

ROTARY, No.73, Steamroller at work £55

188

PICTURING THEIR PAST

Postcards and family history

By Penny Law, Editor of Family History Monthly

It is all too easy to get bogged-down in brown, dusty documents when you are researching your family tree; from birth certificates and newspaper clippings to wills and ancient maps, it can be a long time before you come across any colour. It is this void that the picture postcard so neatly fills.

Collecting postcards was a hugely popular pastime in the early 20th century and the examples which survive today can tell us an enormous amount about the lives and characters of our ancestors. For example, I have a friend who recently discovered two complete postcard albums in almost mint condition in the attic of her late father. The albums had belonged to her grandmother who was evidently an avid collector, and she was delighted to discover that through them

she was able to piece-together the various jaunts and holidays of every family member between 1904 and 1912.

Postcards may even show the family business

The postcards were revealing in two ways, the first of which being that they showed where the family had spent their holidays. To those of you who haven't yet been bitten by the genealogy bug, this may sound fairly unremarkable, but it is notoriously hard to find out about ancestors' leisure time, so any clues as to where they went and what they did to have fun is invaluable. Secondly, the writing

> *"Collecting postcards was a hugely popular pastime in the early 20th century"*

PICTURING THEIR PAST

on the back provided a snapshot into the life of the sender, and possibly that of the person it was being sent to. The very nature of the postcard was infor-

won't have had such extensive collections passed down to us, and we have to compile our own. As a result, when I see a shop or stall selling old post-

> *"The very nature of the postcard was informal, so the messages are often whimsical and quite amusing"*

mal, so the messages are often whimsical and quite amusing. Again, it is near impossible to gauge any sense of a forebear's personality from the traditional documents of family history research, so stumbling across examples of their casual communication is like hitting the jackpot.

However, the majority of us

cards – regardless of where I am, what I'm doing and who I'm with – I can't

> *"It's magical to stumble across a picture postcard showing the church where our ancestors would have married"*

St. Clements Church, Ilford.

10.

help but trawl through the entire lot. The postcards which are of particular interest to family historians are those that depict an ancestral village, or town. It's magical to stumble across a picture postcard showing the church where our ancestors would have married, the park where they would have played, or the pub in which they would have drunk. You may even strike gold and discover a photo of the actual street where your grandparents or great-grandparents once lived.

"Buildings and streets with which my forebears would have been so familiar"

ABINGTON STREET. NORTHAMPTON.

I am a relative novice to family history, but even I have now amassed a collection of over 20 postcards from the turn of the century depicting the buildings and streets with which my forebears would have been so familiar. Coming across place names on old records and then locating them on contemporary maps is an extremely useful way of furthering your research, but it's certainly not as evocative or moving as discovering a photograph of the place on a postcard.

Postcards can give a glimpse of our ancestors lives

OVERSEAS TOPOGRAPHICAL

Please read the following explanation before consulting prices:

Every country listed in this section could support its own catalogue. Many of them produced literally millions of postcards, and although I have now begun to sub-classify many countries, a process which will be continued in future editions of this Catalogue, it must be clearly understood that at best, all one can really do in the pages which follow, is to put the reader in touch with the broad general price area for any particular card.

The degree of classification of any one country is a reflection of the demand for that country. France catalogues in much greater depth than Luxembourg for example, because the demand is there. Readers may like to think about this, when choosing a country to collect? With many countries there exist definite market indications which allow me to list Town and City Street Scenes, while other `non-collected' countries can at present only be covered either with a general `Street Scene' heading, or, in many cases, with just a single price for the whole country!

To achieve a logical presentation, I have in all cases used the term `Street Scenes', but where applicable, e.g in small islands, this is taken to mean all population centres, hut settlements, native villages, dirt-track roads etc. I don't need to be told that there are few `Streets' in Tibet or Nepal - I have deliberately chosen to use this term throughout the listings to achieve a correct balance.

Railway Stations are in all cases taken to be Town or Village stations. It is suggested that main City stations or termini be treated as `General Views', unless of course you are faced with a quite spectacular card. With all Foreign cards you will find a great many which are virtually worthless. These include Beach Scenes • Cathedrals • Churches • Countryside • Gardens • Historic Buildings • Lake Scenes • Landscapes • Mountains • Parks • Religious Buildings • River Scenes • Ruins • Stately Homes • Waterfalls • WW1 Shell Damage • Volcanoes etc.

As far as possible within the confines of a logical presentation, I have listed countries under the name by which they were known at the turn of the century. Where applicable, I have also given the modern name of the country in brackets, followed by the date this name was adopted. (This is not necessarily the date of independence).

Prices...

... are given for both **Unused** and **Used** cards. With **Unused,** prices may be taken as a broad, general average for the classification to which they refer. However, in all classifications there will be some very common cards which are worth much less than the stated figure, whilst on the other hand there will be cards which are worth more. With **Used** cards, prices are for Postcards which are of non philatelic origin, bearing the correct postal rate for the period and distance involved, and with a clear cancel on the address side only. **The price given represents a basic value for any correctly used Postcard of that country.**

It is pointed out that some postally used cards from certain countries or Islands are particularly rare, and may fetch a price considerably in excess of that quoted. In these cases, and where these conditions also apply to unused cards, a + sign has been entered.

The + sign has also been used where a realistic market value has not yet been established. This does not necessarily mean that the Postcard in used form is particularly rare, although certainly worth the price quoted. At best, all one can do within the limitations of a Catalogue of this kind, is to offer the reader a general indication of value for the cards in which he is interested.

Market Report

There are now few unsaleable countries, thanks to the international nature of the hobby. The far east, with China in particular, is on a mission to reclaim its heritage. Russia, Turkey, Greece, Malta, Italy, Cyprus, Norway and even Belgium are all avidly looked for. The Falklands, Seychelles, Mauritius, Tibet, Borneo and the Gulf States are instantly saleable if you can find them. Problematic areas include most of the Americas, North and South Africa are slow to sell and Sweden and Portugal are yet to show any signs of life.

	Unused	Used
ADEN		
South Yemen 1967		£6
Street Scenes	£2	
General Views	£1.50	
AFGHANISTAN		£15+
Ethnic	£5	
Street Scenes	£12	
General Views	£5	
ALBANIA		£3+
Ethnic	£5	
Street Scenes	£6	
General Views	£3	
ALGERIA		£1
Street Scenes	£2	
Ethnic	£2	
General Views	£1	
ANDAMAN ISLANDS		£15
General Views	£5	
ANDORRA		£5+
Street Scenes	£8	
General Views	£2	
ANGOLA		£5
Street Scenes	£6	
General Views	£2	
ANGUILLA		£20+
Street Scenes	£12	
General Views	£8	
ANTIGUA		£8+
Street Scenes	£10	
General Views	£2	
ARGENTINA	£2	£2
Ethnic	£3	
Railways	£8	

	Unused	Used
Street Scenes/Town	£3	
/City	£1.50	
/Rural	£4	
General Views	£1.50	
ASCENSION		£25+
Royal Visit	£25	£100+
General Views	£15	
AUSTRALIA		£1
Aborigines	£10	
Bush Life	£3	
Dairy Industry	£3	
Farming	£3	
Industrial	£8	
Mining	£6	
Railway Stations	£12+	
Sheep Farming	£1.50	
Street Markets	£6	
Timber Industry	£5	
Trades/Workers	£5	
USA Fleet Visit	£18	
Street Scenes/Town	£6	
/City	£3	
/Rural	£8	
General Views	£2	
AUSTRIA		£1
Costume	£1.50	
Railway Stations	£8	
Street Markets	£5	
Gruss Aus	£8	
Street Scenes/Town	£3	
/City	£1	
/Rural	£5	
General Views	£1	
AZORES		£3
Street Scenes	£5	
General Views	£2	
BAHAMAS		£4
Hurricane 1933	£10	
Ethnic	£3	
Street Scenes/Town	£6	
/Rural	£8	
USA coloured views	£2	
General Views	£2	
BAHRAIN		£20+
Street Scenes	£8	
General Views	£5	

Austria, Wien   £3

	Unused	Used
BARBADOS		£5
Railway	£12	
Ethnic	£3	
Street Scenes	£6	
General Views	£3	
BASUTOLAND		
Lesotho 1966	£15+	
Ethnic	£3	
Street Scenes/Town	£8	
/Rural	£12+	
General Views	£3	
BECHUANALAND		
Botswana 1966	£15+	
Ethnic	£5	
Street Scenes	£10+	
General Views	£3	
BELGIAN CONGO		
Zaire 1971		£4
Street Scenes	£6	
General Views	£1.50	
BELGIUM		.50
Costume	£1	
Dog Carts	£4	
Industrial	£6+	
Railway Stations	£8+	
Street Markets	£5	
Steam Trams	£15+	
Trades/Workers	£4	
WW1 Shell Damage	£1	
Street Scenes/Towns	£4	
/City	.50	
General Views	.50	
BERMUDA		£6+
Ethnic	£3	
Street Scenes/Town	£6	
General Views	£2	
BOLIVIA		£5+
Ethnic	£2	
Railways	£6	
Street Scenes/Town	£5	
/Rural	£6	
General Views	£2	
BORNEO		£25+
Street Scenes/Town	£20+	
/Rural	£20+	
Dutch	£6	
BOSNIA & HERZEGOVINA		
Yugoslavia 1929		£2
Street Scenes	£4	
General Views	£2	
BRAZIL		£3
Ethnic	£3	
Railways	£8	

	Unused	Used
Street Scenes/Town	£6	
Street Scenes/City	£2	
General Views	£1	
BRITISH GUIANA		
Guyana 1966		£8
Ethnic	£5	
Sugar Industry	£4	
Street Scenes/Town	£8	
/Rural	£10	
General Views	£3	
BRITISH HONDURAS		
Belize 1973		£15+
Street Scenes/Town	£10+	
/Rural	£15+	
General Views	£6	
BRITISH NEW GUINEA		
Papua New Guinea 1975		£15+
Ethnic	£10+	
Street Scenes	£20	
General Views	£8+	
BRITISH SOMALILAND		
Somalia 1960		£8
Street Scenes	£15	
General Views	£6	
BRITISH VIRGIN ISLANDS		£12
Street Scenes	£15	
General Views	£6	
BRUNEI		£25+
Street Scenes	£12	
General Views	£8	
BULGARIA		£1
Ethnic	£3	
Street Scenes	£4	
General Views	£1	
BURMA		£8
Ethnic	£3	
Street Scenes	£4	
General Views	£2	

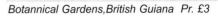

Botannical Gardens,British Guiana Pr. £3

	Unused	Used
CAICOS ISLANDS		£15
Street Scenes	£15+	
General Views	£12	
CAMBODIA		£8+
Kampuchea 1979		
Temples	£1	
Street Scenes	£8+	
General Views	£2	
CAMEROON		£10
Street Scenes	£10	
General Views	£3	
CANADA		£1
Farming	£1.50	
Indians	£6	
Industrial	£5	
Lake Steamers	£3	
Mining	£5	
Railway/CPR Views	£3	
Railway Stations	£8	
Street Markets	£3	
Trades/Workers	£3	
Street Scenes/Town	£4	
/City	£2	
/Rural	£8+	
General Views	£1	
CANAL ZONE		£3
Ethnic	£3	
Panama Canal	£3	
Street Scenes	£8	
General Views	£1.50	
CANARY ISLANDS		£3
Ethnic	£3	
Street Scenes	£4	
General Views	£1.50	
CAPE VERDE ISLANDS		£3
General Views	£3	
CAROLINE ISLANDS		£20
Pelew Islands, Ethnic	£6	
CAYMAN ISLANDS		£15+
General Views	£10	
CEYLON		
Sri Lanka 1972		£2
Ethnic	£3	
Tea Plantations	£3	
Street Scenes/Town	£4	
/City	£2	
Temples	£1.50	
General Views	£2	
CHAD		£6
Street Scenes	£8+	
General Views	£2	
CHATHAM ISLAND		£10+
General Views	£8	
CHILE		£3
Ethnic	£3	

Carlton Hotel, Ceylon, Pr. £4

	Unused	Used
Railways	£10+	
Street Scenes/Town	£5	
/City	£3	
General Views	£2	
CHINA		£8
Ethnic	£5	
Street Scenes/City	£10	
/Towns	£10	
General Views	£5	
Temples/Pagodas	£4	
CHRISTMAS ISLAND		£25+
Atomic Tests	£15	
General Views	£18	
COCOS ISLANDS		£25+
General Views	£18	
COLOMBIA		£4
Ethnic	£3	
Railways	£10+	
Street Scenes	£5	
General Views	£2	
COMORO ISLANDS		£8+
General Views	£3	
COOK ISLANDS		£12+
Street Scenes	£10	
General Views	£8	
CORFU		£2
Street Scenes	£5	
General Views	£1	
COSTA RICA		£6+
Ethnic	£3	
Street Scenes	£8	
General Views	£3	
CRETE		£5
Ethnic	£10	
Street Scenes	£12	
General Views	£6	
CUBA		£2
Street Scenes	£4	
General Views	£2	

Cyprus Pr. £4

	Unused	Used
CURACAO		
Netherlands Antilles		£5+
Street Scenes	£6	
General Views	£1	
CYPRUS		£8
Ethnic	£8	
Street Scenes	£15	
General Views	£6	
CZECHOSLOVAKIA		£1
Street Scenes	£3	
General Views	£1	
DAHOMEY		
Benin 1975		£6
Street Scenes	£8	
General Views	£3	
DANISH WEST INDIES		
Virgin Islands/USA 1917		£15+
Ethnic	£5	
Street Scenes	£8	
General Views	£3	
DANZIG		
Poland 1945		£2
Street Scenes	£6	
General Views	£2	
DENMARK		£1
Costume	£1	
Street Scenes/Town	£3	
/City	£1	
General Views	£1	
DOMINICA		£6
General Views	£3	
DOMINICAN REPUBLIC		£2
General Views	£3	
DUTCH GUIANA		
Suriname 1975		£5
General Views	£3	

Budwitz, Czechoslovakia Pr. £3

	Unused	Used
DUTCH NEW GUINEA		
Street Scenes	£6	
General Views	£3	
EASTER ISLAND		£25
General Views	£8	
ECUADOR		£4
Ethnic	£4	
Railways	£10+	
Street Scenes/Town	£6	
/City	£3	
General Views	£2	
EGYPT		£1
Ethnic	£2	
Street Scenes	£2	
General Views	£1	
ELLICE ISLANDS		
Tuvalu 1978		£10+
Street Scenes	£15	
General Views	£8	
EL SALVADOR		£4
Ethnic	£3	
Railway	£10+	
Street Scenes	£5	
General Views	£2	
ERITREA		
Ethiopia 1952		£3
Ethnic	£4	
Street Scenes	£8	
General Views	£1.50	
ESTONIA		
Russia 1940		£6
Ethnic	£3	
Street Scenes	£8	
General Views	£2	
ETHIOPIA		£5+
Ethnic	£3	
Street Scenes	£6	
General Views	£2	

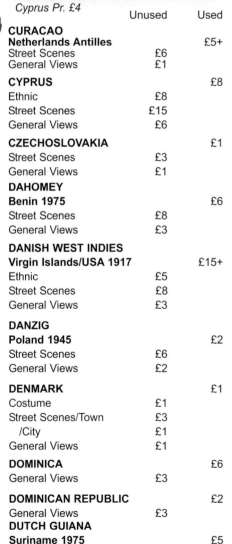

	Unused	Used

Dinan, France £3

FALKLAND ISLANDS — £50+

Events	£40	
Penguins & Birds	£8	
Sheep Farming	£25	
Whaling	£40	
Street Scenes	£25	
General Views	£20	

FANNING ISLAND — £15+

General Views	£8+	

FAROE ISLANDS — £10+

General Views	£8	

Fiji Pr. £4

FIJI — £5

Ethnic	£6	
StreetScenes	£10+	
General Views	£3-£5	

FINLAND — £3

Costume	£3	
Street Scenes/Town	£5	
/City	£2	
General Views	£1.50	

FIUME
Yugoslavia 1947 — £5

Street Scenes	£6	
General Views	£1.50	

FORMOSA
Taiwan — £12+

Street Scenes	£10+	
General Views	£5	

FRENCH GUIANA — £4

General Views	£3	

FRENCH GUINEA
Guinea 1958 — £4

General Views	£4	

FRENCH OCEANIA — £10+

Street Scenes	£8	
General Views	£2	

FRENCH SOMALILAND
Djibouti 1977 — £5

Street Scenes	£8	
General Views	£2	

FRENCH SOUDAN
Mali 1960 — £3

Street Scenes	£5	
General Views	£2	

FRANCE — .50

Animal Markets	£6	
Costume	.50	
Dog Carts	£60+	
Farming	£3	
Fetes	£6	
Fishing Industry	£3	
Street/Fish Markets	£6	
Industrial	£5	
Mining	£5	
Railway Stations	£8	
Synagogues	£25	
Trades/Workers	£6	
Watermills	£3	
Windmills	£5	
Street Scenes/Villages	£8+	
/Town	£4+	
/City	£1	

GABON — £4

Street Scenes	£10	
General Views	£2	

GAMBIA — £8+

Street Scenes	£8	
General Views	£3	

GERMAN EAST AFRICA — £10+
Burundi 1962/Rwanda 1962/Tanzania 1961

Ethnic	£5	
Occupation 1914/18	£6	
Street Scenes	£8	
General Views	£3	

	Unused	Used

GERMAN NEW GUINEA
Papua New Guinea 1975 — £20+
Ethnic — £8
Street Scenes — £10
General Views — £4

GERMAN SOUTH WEST AFRICA
Namibia — £8+
Ethnic — £8
Street Scenes — £10

D.-O.-Afrika. Tabora.   Im Holzmannlager.

German East Africa, Pr. £3

General Views — £3

GERMANY — £1
Animal Markets — £6
Costume — £1.50
Farming — £1.50
Industrial — £5
Mining — £4
Railway Stations — £8
Rhine Steamers — £3
Street Markets — £6
Synagogues — £25
Trades/Workers — £6
Street Scenes/Town — £4
    /City — £1
General Views — .50

GIBRALTAR — £1
Street Scenes — £2
General Views — .50

GILBERT ISLANDS
Kiribati 1979 — £20+
Street Scenes — £12
General Views — £8

GOLD COAST
Ghana 1957 — £6
Ethnic — £6
Railway — £10
Street Scenes — £8
General Views — £3

GREECE — £3
Ethnic — £4
Postal Stationery — £8
Street Scenes — £8
General Views — £2

GREENLAND — £20+
Ethnic — £6
General Views — £5

GRENADA — £5+
Street Scenes — £6
General Views — £2

GUADELOUPE — £3
Street Scenes — £8
General Views — £2

GUAM — £10+
Street Scenes — £8
General Views — £4

GUATEMALA — £4
Street Scenes — £6
General Views — £2

HAITI — £3
Street Scenes — £6
General Views — £3

HAWAII — £5
Ethnic — £4
Street Scenes colour — £3
Street Scenes photo — £10
General Views — £2

HELIGOLAND — £2
Street scenes — £6
General Views — £2

HONDURAS — £4
Ethnic — £4
Railway — £10
Street Scenes — £8
General Views — £3

HONG KONG — £6
Ethnic — £6
Peak Railway — £5
Street Scenes Photo — £15
Street Scenes colour — £8
General Views — £5

HUNGARY — £2
Ethnic — £3
Street Scenes — £4
General Views — £1

ICELAND — £10+
Ethnic — £5
Street Scenes — £8
General Views — £3

	Unused	Used
INDIA		£1
British Rule/Barracks etc.	£2	
Ethnic	£3	
Holy Sites	£1	
Court Size	£8	
Street Scenes	£3	
General Views	£1.50	
NWFP Photographic	£3	
IRAQ		£6
British Occupation	£4	
Street Scenes	£8	
General Views	£2	

India Pr.   £3

ITALY		.50
Costume	£1	
Industrial	£10	
Railway Stations	£15	
River Steamers	£3	
Street Markets	£12	
Trades/Workers	£3	
Street Scenes/Town	£5+	
/City	.50	
Villages	£10	
IVORY COAST		£8
Street Scenes	£10	
General Views	£2	
JAMAICA		£3
Ethnic	£3	
Railway	£10	
Sugar Industry	£3	
Street Scenes	£6	
General Views	£2	
JAPAN		£2
Ethnic/Geishas	£2	
Shrines/Temples	£1.50	
Yokohama Earthquake	£3	
Street Scenes/City	£4	
/Towns	£5	
General Views	£1	

	Unused	Used
JAVA		£3
Street Scenes	£5	
General Views	£3	
KENYA		£4
Ethnic	£6	
Street Scenes	£6	
General Views	£3	
KOREA		£8+
Street Scenes	£8	
General Views	£3	
KUWAIT		£20+
Street Scenes	£12	
General Views	£5	

Honolulu, Hawaii, £3

LABUAN		£20+
Street Scenes	£15+	
General Views	£10	
LAOS		£10
Street Scenes	£10	
General Views	£3	
LATVIA		
Russia 1940		£4
Ethnic	£5	
Street Scenes	£6	
General Views	£3	
LEBANON		£5
Ethnic	£3	
Street Scenes	£4	
General Views	£1.50	
LIBERIA		£10+
Street Scenes	£8	
General Views	£2	
LIBYA		£2
General Views	£2	
LIECHTENSTEIN		£3
Street Scenes	£6	
General Views	£2	

Brindisi Port, Italy. Pr. £5

Nagasaki, Japan Pr. £4

	Unused	Used
LITHUANIA		
Russia 1940		£5
Ethnic	£6	
Street Scenes	£3	
General Views	£2	
LUXEMBOURG		.50
Street Scenes	£3	
General Views	.50	
MACAO		£25+
Street Scenes	£25	
General Views	£10	
MADAGASCAR		£3
Street Scenes	£6	
General Views	£1.50	
MADEIRA		£3
Street Scenes	£3	
General Views	£1.50	
MALAYA		
Malaysia 1963		£6
Ethnic	£4	
Railways	£12	
Rubber Industry	£3	
Street Scenes	£8	
General Views	£2	
MALDIVE ISLANDS		£10+
General Views	£8	
MALTA		£1
Ethnic	£3	
Street Scenes/RP	£6	
/Coloured	£1	
General Views	£1	
Early Undivided back	£4	
MARTINIQUE		£3
Volcano 1902	£3	
Street Scenes	£8	
General Views	£1.50	
MAURITANIA		£3
Street Scenes	£8	
General Views	£2	

	Unused	Used
MAURITIUS		£8
Railways	£15	
Street Scenes	£12	
General Views	£5	
MEXICO		£2
Ethnic	£3	
Railways	£10	
Street Scenes	£4	
General Views	£1.50	
MIDDLE CONGO		
Congo 1960		£6
Street Scenes	£8	
General Views	£2	
MOLUCCA ISLANDS		
General Views	£5	
MONACO		.50
Street Scenes	£1.50	
General Views	.50	
MONGOLIA		£20+
General Views	£6	
Ethnic	£6	
MONTENEGRO		
Yugoslavia 1929		£5
Street Scenes	£8	
General Views	£1.50	
MONTSERRAT		£12
General Views	£8	
MOROCCO		£1
Street Scenes	£3	
General Views	£1	
Ethnic	£2	
MOZAMBIQUE		£4
Street Scenes	£5	
General Views	£1	
MUSCAT & OMAN		
Oman 1970		£30+
Street Scenes	£12	
General Views	£6	
NAURU		£25+
General Views	£10	

Mombasa, Kenya, Pr. £3

	Unused	Used
NEPAL		£20+
Ethnic	£6	
General Views	£5	
NETHERLANDS		.50
Canals	£1	
Costume	.50	
Customs & Traditions	£1	
Industrial	£3	
Railway Stations	£6	
Street Markets	£4	
Trades/Workers	£3	
Windmills	£1.50	
Street Scenes/Village	£6	
/Town	£2	
/City	.50	
General Views	.50	
NEVIS		£10+
General Views	£8	
NEW CALEDONIA		£10+
Street Scenes	£8	
General Views	£3	
NEWFOUNDLAND		£6
Fishing Industry	£6	
Railway Stations	£12	
Street Scenes	£10	
General Views	£5	
NEW HEBRIDES		£15+
Vanuata 1980		
Street Scenes	£10+	
General Views	£5	

Monrovia, Liberia Pr. £2

	Unused	Used
NEW ZEALAND		£1
Dairy Industry	£3	
Farming	£1.50	
Industrial	£6	
Maoris	£4	
Railway Stations	£10+	
Sheep Farming	£1	
Street Markets	£6	
Trades/Workers	£5	
Street Scenes/Town	£6	
/City	£3	
General Views	£1.50	
NICARAGUA		£6
Ethnic	£6	
Railways	£12+	
Street Scenes	£8+	
General Views	£3	
NIGER		£3
Ethnic	£8	
Street Scenes	£6	
General Views	£2	
NIGERIA		£3
Ethnic	£3	
Railways	£8	
Street Scenes	£6	
General Views	£3	
NIUE		£15+
General Views	£8	
NORFOLK ISLAND		£20+
General Views	£18	
Street Scenes	£20	
NORTH BORNEO		
Sabah 1964		£20+
Ethnic	£6	
Street Scenes	£15+	
General Views	£6	
NORTHERN RHODESIA		
Zambia 1964		£6
Ethnic	£4	
Railways	£15+	
Street Scenes	£8	
General Views	£2	
NORWAY		£1
Costume	£1	
Street Scenes/Town	£5	
/City	£3	
General Views	£1	
NYASALAND		
Malawi 1964		£4
Ethnic	£4	
Street Scenes	£6	
General Views	£3	

Monaco, Pr. £2

Nepal, Ethnic, Pr. £6

Nigeria Race course and Cricket Pr. £6

	Unused	Used
OUBANGUI-CHARI		
Central African Republic 1960		£5
General Views	£3	
PALESTINE		
Israel 1948		£1
British Occupation	£6	
Ethnic	£2	
Religious Sites	.50	
Street Scenes	£6	
General Views	£1	
PANAMA	£4	£4
Ethnic	£3	
Railways	£10+	
Street Scenes	£5	
General Views	£1.50	
PAPUA NEW GUINEA		£10
Street Scenes	£10	
General Views	£6	
PARAGUAY		£3
Ethnic	£4	
Railways	£12+	
Street Scenes	£8	
General Views	£2	
PEMBA ISLAND		£20+
Ethnic	£6	
General Views	£6	
PERIM ISLAND		£15+
General Views	£5	
PERSIA		
Iran 1935		£10
Street Scenes	£12	
General Views	£6	
PERU		£5
Ethnic	£5	
Railways	£10+	
Street Scenes	£6+	
General Views	£2	
PHILIPPINES		£3
Street Scenes	£8	
General Views	£2	

	Unused	Used
PITCAIRN ISLAND		£40+
Ethnic	£20	
General Views	£15	
POLAND		£3
Ethnic	£2	
Street Scenes	£5	
General Views	£3	
PORTUGAL		£1
Costume	£1.50	
Industrial	£4	
Railway Stations	£8	
Street Markets	£5	
Trades/Workers	£4	
Street Scenes/Town	£4	
/City	£1	
General Views	£1	
PORTUGUESE GUINEA		
Guinea-Bissau 1974		£5
Street Scenes	£8	
General Views	£1.50	
PORTUGUESE TIMOR		
East Timor		£5
Street Scenes	£8	
General Views	£2	
PUERTO RICO		£4
Street Scenes	£10	
General Views	£4	
REUNION		£6

	Unused	Used
Ethnic	£6	
Street Scenes	£8	
General Views	£3	
ROMANIA		£1
Ethnic	£3	
Street Scenes	£6	
General Views	£2	
RUSSIA		£3
Costume	£3	
Ethnic	£8	
Industrial	£8	
Railway Stations	£15	
Street Markets	£15	
Trades/Workers	£15	
Street Scenes/Town	£8	
/City	£3	
General Views	£4	
ST. HELENA		£12+
Boer War	£20	
Street Scenes	£5	
General Views	£3	
ST. KITTS		£8+
Street Scenes	£10	
General Views	£4	
ST. LUCIA		£8+
Street Scenes	£8	
General Views	£3	
ST. PIERRE & MIQUELON		£10+
Street Scenes	£10	
General Views	£4	
ST. THOMAS & PRINCE ISLAND		£6+
Street Scenes	£6	
General Views	£2	
ST. VINCENT		£8+
Street Scenes	£8	
General Views	£3	
SAMOA		£12+
Ethnic	£6	
Street Scenes	£12	
General Views	£5	
SAN MARINO	£2	£2
Street Scenes	£4	
General Views	£2	
SARAWAK		£25+
Ethnic	£10	
Street Scenes	£20	
General Views	£10	
SARDINIA		£2
Street Scenes	£5	
General Views	£2	

Callao: "Avenida Saenz Peña" y "Plaza Casanave," (Perú)

Puerto Rico Pr. £4

	Unused	Used
SAUDI ARABIA		£15+
Street Scenes	£8	
General Views	£4	
SENEGAL		£3
Street Scenes	£5	
General Views	£2	
SERBIA		
Yugoslavia 1929		£3
Ethnic	£3	
Street Scenes	£5	
General Views	£2	
SEYCHELLES		£25+
Street Scenes	£20+	
General Views	£10	
SIAM		
Thailand		£8+
Street Scenes	£10+	
General Views	£3	
SIERRA LEONE		£5
Ethnic	£4	
Railways	£10+	
Street Scenes	£6	
General Views	£3	
SIKKIM		
India 1975		£20+
General Views	£5	
Ethnic	£8	
SINGAPORE		£6
Ethnic	£5	
Railway Stations	£15+	
Street Scenes	£8	
General Views	£4	
SOLOMON ISLANDS		£20+
Street Scenes	£10+	
General Views	£6	
SOMALILAND		
Somalia 1960		£20+
Street Scenes	£8	
General Views	£3	
SOUTH AFRICA		£1
Ethnic	£2	

	Unused	Used
Industrial	£5	
Mining	£5	
Railways	£8	
Railway Stations	£8	
Trekking	£2	
Street Scenes/Town	£4	
/City	£1.50	
General Views	£1.50	

Spain Pr . £6

SOUTHERN RHODESIA
Zimbabwe 1980   £5
City Street Scenes   £6
City Buildings   £4
Town Street scenes   £12+
General Views   £3

SPAIN   £1
Bullfighting   £2
Costume   £1
Industrial   £4
Railway Stations   £8
Street Markets   £5
Trades/Workers   £3
Street Scenes/Towns   £4
/City   £2
General Views   £1

SPANISH GUINEA
Equatorial Guinea 1968   £4
Street Scenes   £8
General Views   £3

SUDAN   £4
Ethnic   £4
Street Scenes   £8
General Views   £2

SUMATRA   £3
Street Scenes   £6
General Views   £1

SWAZILAND   £10+
Ethnic   £4
Street Scenes   £8
General Views   £4

SWEDEN   £1
Costume   .50

Switzerland Hotel R/P. £4

Street Scenes/Town   £3
/City   £1
General Views   .50
SWITZERLAND
Costume   £1
Customs & Traditions £1
Industrial   £3
Lake Steamers   £2
Mountain Railways   £2
Railway Stations   £8
Trades/Workers   £5
Street Scenes/Town   £3
/City   £1
General Views   .50

SYRIA   £3
Street Scenes   £4
General Views   £1.50

TANGANYIKA
Tanzania 1961   £6
Ethnic   £5
Street Scenes   £8
General Views   £3

TASMANIA   £3
Street Scenes   £6
General Views   £1.50

THURSDAY ISLAND   £10+
General Views   £8

Sierra Leone Pr. £3

	Unused	Used
TIBET		£40+
Ethnic	£12+	
General Views	£30+	
TIMOR		£15+
Street Scenes	£6	
General Views	£3	
TOBAGO		£5+
Street Scenes	£6	
General Views	£3	
TOGO		£6
Ethnic	£6	
Street Scenes	£5	
General Views	£4	
TONGA		£15+
Ethnic	£12	
General Views	£8	
TRANSJORDAN		
Jordan 1946		£4
Street Scenes	£6	
General Views	£1.50	
TRINIDAD		£3
Ethnic	£3	
Oil Industry	£5	
Street Scenes	£6	
General Views	£3	
TRISTAN DA CUNHA **(PRE 1928)**		£250+
Later issues	£25+	
TUNISIA		£2+
Street Scenes	£3	
General Views	£1	
TURKEY		£5+
Ethnic	£4	
Street Scenes/town	£6	
Street Scenes/city	£3	
General Views	£1.50	
TURKS ISLANDS		£20+
Street Scenes	£12	
General Views	£12	
UGANDA		£5+
Ethnic	£4	
Street Scenes	£6	
General Views	£3	
UPPER VOLTA		
Burkina 1984		£5+
Street Scenes	£8	
General Views	£1.50	
URUGUAY		£3
Ethnic	£4	
Railways	£10	
Street Scenes/Town	£5	
/City	£3	
General Views	£1.50	
U.S.A.		£1

Constantinopole, Turkey. £3

	Unused	Used
Cattle	.50	
Indians	£6	
Industrial	£3	
Mining	£5	
Railway Stations	£6	
Steamboats	£3	
Street Scenes/Town	£4	
/City	£1	
General Views	.50	
VENEZUELA		£4
Ethnic	£5	
Railways	£10	
Street Scenes	£5	
General Views	£1.50	
VIETNAM		£3
Ethnic	£6	
Street Scenes	£8	
General Views	£3	
YEMEN		£5+
Street Scenes	£6	
General Views	£4	
YUGOSLAVIA		£2
Ethnic	£3	
Street Scenes	£5	
General Views	£1.50	
ZANZIBAR		£8
Ethnic	£8	
Street Scenes	£6	
General Views	£2	

Florida, USA P. £4

IMPORTANT. Prices quoted are for complete, clear postmarks in every instance. Partial or indistinct strikes, generally have very little value.

CIRCULAR DATE STAMP

English type - 50p
The most common of all postmarks

Scottish type - 75p upwards

SINGLE RING

SQUARED CIRCLES

Three different types
£1 each
For lesser used types -
£2 upwards to £40

50p
upwards

Small 'thimble'
circular ring
£1 upwards

DUPLEX

£1 upwards
Certain obscure or limited types
may be worth up to £10 each

MACHINE CANCELLATIONS £1-£3

Two different examples of the E (Crown) R Type. Used in
London (£5) Liverpool (£20)

STAMPS ON POSTCARDS

In response to many enquiries we receive about the value of Stamps found on Postcards, it must be pointed out that the picture postcard invariably carried the minimum postage rate, and these low-denomination Stamps are virtually worthless. Realistically, the only value in a used card would be if it has been stamped and posted from an 'unusual' country, or small island, or if it bears a cancellation of some interest.

INLAND POSTAGE RATES

1 October 1870 - 3 June 1918 - $^{1}/_{2}$d
3 June 1918 - 13 June 1921 - 1d
13 June 1921 - 24 May 1922 - 1$^{1}/_{2}$d
24 May 1922 - 1 May 1940 - 1d

FIRST DAY OF ISSUE

QUEEN VICTORIA

$^{1}/_{2}$d Blue Green	17 April 1900	£500

KING EDWARD VII

$^{1}/_{2}$d Blue Green	1 January 1902	£40
1d Red	1 January 1902	£40
$^{1}/_{2}$d Yellow Green	26 November 1904	£35

KING GEORGE V

$^{1}/_{2}$d Green (three-quarter profile, hair dark)	22 June 1911	£30
1d Red (three-quarter profile, Lion unshaded)	22 June 1911	£40
$^{1}/_{2}$d Green (three-quarter profile, Hair light)	1 January 1912	£40
1d Red (three-quarter profile, Lion shaded)	1 January 1912	£45
*British Empire Exhibition 1924. (1d Red)	23 April 1924	£15
*British Empire Exhibition 1925. (1d Red)	9 May 1925	£30
U.P.U Congress 1929 ($^{1}/_{2}$d or 1d)	10 May 1929	£12
$^{1}/_{2}$d Green	19 November 1934	£5
1d Red	24 September 1934	£5
Silver Jubilee 1935. ($^{1}/_{2}$d or 1d)	7 May 1935	£6

* Postcards bearing Wembley Park 1924 or 1925 handstamp or slogan cancel on exhibition cards would justify a premium.

KING EDWARD VIII

$^{1}/_{2}$d Green	1 September 1936	£6
1d Red	14 September 1936	£12

KING GEORGE VI

$^{1}/_{2}$d Green	10 May 1937	£1
1d Red	10 May 1937	£1

POSTMARKS ON POSTCARDS

This is a vast and complex field, and part of the much wider area of Philately. There are thousands of different postal markings and stamps to be found on the backs of picture postcards, and indeed there is a similar number of specialised philatelic books devoted to all aspects of this subject.

In a postcard Catalogue of this kind, it is only possible to give a very rough indication of price for postmarks likely to be found on picture postcards. Readers requiring more specialised information or catalogues are referred to any good stamp dealer, or to one of the many books available on the subject.

CACHETS

50p

Handstamps applied other than by the Official PO. Other common types are 'Summit of Snowdon', "Beachy Head'

METER MARKS

50p
Normally meant for business use

POSTAGE DUES

From £1 upwards
Surcharge marks for under-paid mail, many varieties

EXHIBITIONS

Edinburgh 1908
£6

Crystal Palace Code 3
(below date) £20

A complex field where price depends upon the particular exhibition and date
£1. - £50

(i)

(ii)

(iii)

EXAMINATION MARKS

Post Office Examiner's marks applied to wrongly sorted mail. Usually stamped in black but type (iii) sometimes found in violet. 75p - £2 each
N.B. There is a larger type as (iii) which was used for checking the bulk posting of circulars, etc. Price 50p each

---

SKELETONS

A temporary hand-stamp used for a limited period. Of varying sizes usually 27 - 39 mm in diameter. Price subject to wide fluctuation £3-£10 upwards

RUBBER DATE-STAMPS

often in blue or violet, used by
smaller offices
£3 - £10 if superb coloured

ISLANDS

Circular Date Stamps Examples shown,
Gorey £3, Sandwich Shetland £5. Others
such as Lundy Island £40,
St. Kilda £25. Chief offices of Jersey,
Guernsey and I.O.M are common

RECEIVED FROM H M SHIP

£1.50
Naval security markings

DUMB CANCELS

£1.50
Naval security markings

SLOGANS

50p upwards
Mostly common, but there are exceptions amongst many hundreds of different types

ARMY & FIELD POST OFFICES

A popular specialist field - with wide price
fluctuations

Field Post Office G
France 1915
£1 upwards

P.B.2
1919 Archangel
£25

AUTOGRAPHS
by John Priestley

RT. HON. A.J. BALFOUR, M.P.

Above: A postcard hand signed by Arthur J. Balfour valued at £100

WHAT IS AN AUTOGRAPH REALLY WORTH?

It is worth remembering a signature is always an autograph but an autograph is not always a signature.

What we are concerned with here is signatures, in autograph books, which is the most common and cheapest form, on photographs and postcards, and on letters which could be either typed, written by a secretary and then signed or completely hand written. It must be remembered that the vast majority of autographs, especially on photographs and postcards will not be original, many will be machine, rubber stamped, signed by a third party, often a secretary or simply forged since the middle of the twentieth century the autopen machine has further complicated collecting as the signatures often can not be separated from genuine autograph unless you have two copies, the autopen signatures will be identical the handwritten ones will be slightly different as you can never sign two identical signatures. As with postcards, the value of an autograph is dependant on popularity and scarcity.

Here we have listed a cross section of Stars/Celebrities, some very old and some not so old, which we hope will help in explaining values of autographs.

GLOSSARY

Sig - Signature, in an autograph book or on a card, remember a signature alone on the back of a postcard is little better than an autograph in an autograph book.

Photo- Signature, on the front of a Postcard or Photo of the subject.

L.S. A letter written by a third party, usually a secretary and then signed by the subject.

T.L.S. A typed letter signed by the subject

A.L.S. A letter completely handwritten and signed by the subject. A Postcard hand written and signed would be priced about the same.

ARTISTS	Sig	Photo	T.L.S.	A.L.S.
Peter Blake	10	20	30	40
Salvador Dali	80	200	120	200
Tracy Emin	50	200	200	300
David Hockney	20	80	120	150
Damian Hirst	50	100	120	200
Edwin Landseer	20	-	40	100
Frederick Leighton	20	-	40	40
John Everett Millass	30	200	60	120
Henry Moore	40	100	80	140
Pablo Picasso	300	1000	800	1500
David Shepherd	10	20	30	40
Louis Wain	100	400	300	500
Frank Lloyd Wright	100	250	200	30
AUTHORS	**Sig**	**Photo**	**T.L.S.**	**A.L.S.**
J M Barrie	40	150	80	120
Enid Blyton	50	200	100	200
Michael Bond	5	20	20	30
Agatha Christie	100	350	250	350
Charles Dickens	150	-	500	800
Arthur Conan Doyle	80	250	150	250
Carol Ann Duffy	5	15	15	25
Ian Fleming	500	1500	1500	2000
Thomas Hardy	150	350	250	450
Rudyard Kirling	40	150	100	150
Alastair Maclean	40	120	80	100
J D Salinger	800	-	4000	4000
Leo Tolstoy	800	3000	1000	3000
AVIATION/SPACE	**Sig**	**Photo**	**T.L.S.**	**A.L.S.**
Samuel F Cody	40	140	120	180
Yuri Gagarin	80	200	160	300
Amy Johnson	50	120	150	300
Charles Lindbergh	250	1500	1000	2000
Patrick Moore	5	10	10	20
Helen Sharman	5	20	20	30
Igor Sikorsky	40	80	80	100
Claude Graham-White	25	70	90	100
Frank Whittle	50	120	100	150
Orville Wright	300	1200	800	1800
Wilbur Wright	1000	6000	3000	8000
ENTERTAINERS	**Sig**	**Photo**	**T.L.S.**	**A.L.S.**
Josephine Baker	80	150	150	250
Jeremy Brett	30	60	50	80
Clint Eastwood	20	40	50	100

ENTERTAINERS Cont'd	Sig	Photo	T.L.S.	A.L.S.
Errol Flynn	100	200	250	350
William Hartnell	60	100	100	150
Audrey Hepburn	70	150	150	200
Katherine Hepburn	80	200	100	200
George Lazenby	20	40	50	80
David Niven	30	80	80	100
Flora Robson	5	20	20	30
Terry Thomas	50	80	80	120
Kenneth Williams	50	100	100	150
Orson Welles	80	150	120	200
Al Pacino	10	30	40	80
Brad Pitt	20	50	100	100
George Robey	2	15	20	30
Ginger Rogers	20	60	60	80
Elizabeth Taylor	100	500	300	600
Ellen Terry	5	30	30	40
Richard Todd	5	20	20	30
Patrick Troughton	60	120	120	170
John Wayne	500	1000	1000	1500
MILITARY	**Sig**	**Photo**	**T.L.S.**	**A.L.S.**
Douglas Bader	40	100	120	150
Albert Ball V.C.	300	600	600	800
John Churchill	300	-	600	1000
Alexander Haigh	30	80	100	150
Robert E Lee	1000	3500	3500	5000
Bernard Montgomery	50	150	150	200
William Reid V.C.	10	30	30	40
Irwin Rommel	200	400	400	600
Norman Schwarzkoff	10	50	50	70
Garnet Wolseley	15	80	100	150
POLITICS	**Sig**	**Photo**	**T.L.S.**	**A.L.S.**
Tony Blair	10	20	20	40
Gordon Brown	10	20	20	40
Arthur J Balfour	25	100	60	100
Winston Churchill	500	1500	1000	1500
Benjamin Disreali	80	80	150	300
Mohandas Gandhi	250	3000	1800	3000
William Gladstone	20	100	-	100
Edward Heath	10	20	20	30
John F Kennedy	700	1500	1500	2500
Adolf Hitler	700	1500	1000	3000
Robert Peel	10	-	100	150
Spencer Percival	80	-	150	300
Theodore Roosevelt	100	1000	1000	1500
Margaret Thatcher	20	60	80	150

	Sig	Photo	T.L.S.	A.L.S.
Robert Walpole	40	-	200	400

SCIENCE	Sig	Photo	T.L.S.	A.L.S.
Francis Crick	30	100	100	150
Frederick Banting	200	600	600	900
Marie Curie	800	2500	3000	3500
Albert Einsteiin	700	3000	4000	5000
Michael Faraday	100	500	200	400
Sigmund Freud	800	4000	1500	3500
Joseph Lister	100	-	200	400
Guglielmo Marconi	100	300	300	400
Robert Oppenheimer	400	1000	1200	2000
Louis Pasteur	350	2000	700	1000
Frederick Treeves	40	250	200	250
James Watt	300	-	-	1200

MUSIC(CLASSICAL)	Sig	Photo	T.L.S.	A.L.S.
John Barbirolli	10	30	30	50
Adrian Boult	10	30	30	40
Benjamin Britten	80	200	200	300
Aaron Copland	40	100	150	200
W S Gilbert	120	400	250	400
Fritz Kreisler	40	80	80	100
Gustau Mahler	300	4000	1000	2000
Ignasi Paderewski	80	200	150	200
John Philip Souza	80	200	150	250
Arthus Sullivan	100	500	250	400
Michael Tippett	20	40	40	80
Michael Walton	40	100	100	200

MUSIC(OPERA)	Sig	Photo	T.L.S.	A.L.S.
Clara Butt	10	30	30	40
Maria Callas	300	800	500	700
Enrico Carusso	200	600	300	600
Kathleen Ferrier	100	200	200	250
Jenny Lind	50	-	-	150
Nellie Melba	40	100	100	150
Peter Pears	20	50	40	60
Lily Pons	40	120	80	100
Louisa Tetrazzi	20	70	90	120
Richard Tauber	20	50	50	80

MUSIC(POPULAR)	Sig	Photo	T.L.S.	A.L.S.
Beatles	2000	5000	-	-
Bob Dylan	80	150	200	400
Jimmy Hendrix	500	1500	1500	2000
Elton John	10	30	30	60
Oscar Peterson	10	20	20	40
Cole Porter	100	700	200	500
Elvis Presley	400	1000	1000	2000

Music pop Cont'd	Sig	Photo	T.L.S.	A.L.S.
Bruce Springsteen	50	100	100	150
Tina Turner	10	30	30	50
SPORT(CRICKET)	**Sig**	**Photo**	**T.L.S.**	**A.L.S.**
Ian Botham	5	10	20	30
Geoffrey Boycott	5	10	10	20
Donald Bradman	30	80	100	150
C B Fry	40	150	100	150
W G Grace	100	400	300	400
Walter Hammond	20	70	60	100
Tom Hayward	50	150	-	200
Douglas Jardine	40	150	100	150
Harold Larwood	30	150	100	150
Malcolm Marshall	20	50	60	80
Garfield Sobers	10	20	20	40
Pelham Warner	20	80	60	80
SPORT(FOOTBALL)	**Sig**	**Photo**	**T.L.S.**	**A.L.S.**
Alan Ball	25	60	60	80
Gordon Banks	10	20	20	30
David Beckham	10	30	40	60
Bobby Charlton	10	20	30	40
Dixie Dean	30	80	800	100
Roger Hunt	10	20	30	40
Stanley Matthews	30	60	60	80
Bobby Moore	200	350	400	500
Bob Paisley	30	60	50	80
Alf Ramsey	50	100	80	120
Wayne Rooney	20	40	40	60
Bill Shankly	30	60	50	80
SPORT(GOLF)	**Sig**	**Photo**	**T.L.S.**	**A.L.S.**
Seve Ballesteros	10	20	30	50
Nick Faldo	10	20	30	40
Walter Hagan	75	150	100	200
Tony Jacklin	10	20	20	30
Robert Jones(Jnr)	300	700	700	1000
Tom Morris(Snr)	400	800	800	1200
Jack Nicklaus	10	30	40	60
Greg Norman	10	20	20	30
Gary Player	10	30	40	60
Gene Sarazan	10	20	20	30
Tom Watson	10	20	20	30
Tiger Woods	80	150	150	200
SPORT(MOTOR)	**Sig**	**Photo**	**T.L.S.**	**A.L.S.**
Jenson Button	10	30	30	40
Bruce McLaren	100	150	200	300
Stirling Moss	10	20	20	40

Sport Motor Cont'd	Sig	Photo	T.L.S.	A.L.S.
Alain Prost	10	20	20	40
Lewis Hamilton	10	30	30	40
Barry Sheen	30	50	40	60
Michael Schumacher	20	50	70	100
Ayrton Senna	150	350	400	500
Jackie Stewart	10	20	20	40
John Surtees	10	20	20	30

SPORT(VARIOUS)	Sig	Photo	T.L.S.	A.L.S.
Lance Armstrong	20	50	50	70
Roger Bannnister	10	30	30	50
Bjorn Borg	10	20	20	40
Chris Hoy	5	10	10	20
Carl Lewis	10	20	20	30
Joe Louis	80	250	250	350
Jessie Owens	100	300	300	500
Babe Ruth	1500	5000	4000	5000
John L Sulivan	300	1000	1000	2000
Venus Williams	10	30	30	40

PEOPLE OF INTEREST	Sig	Photo	T.L.S.	A.L.S.
Hawley H Crippen	100	-	350	600
Joseph Fry	40	-	80	120
Edmund Hillery	20	50	50	80
Billy Graham	30	50	80	100
Reg Kray	20	50	50	75
Hiram Maxim	50	200	200	250
Fridjof Nansen	80	350	300	600
Lee Harvey Oswald	1500	-	5500	8000
Robert F Scott	200	-	300	800
Haile Selassie	150	900	400	600
Albert Schweitzer	100	400	300	400
John Stuart Mill	80	-	-	400
Victoria(Queen)	100	1000	200	400
Brigham Young	200	1500	800	1500

Sig - Signature, in an autograph book or on a card, remember a signature alone on the back of a postcard is little better than an autograph in an autograph book.
L.S. A letter written by a third party, usually a secretary and then signed by the subject.
T.L.S. A typed letter signed by the subject
A.L.S. A letter completely handwritten and signed by the subject. A Postcard hand-written and signed would be priced about the same.

INDEX TO ADVERTISERS

Advertising postcard listings start on page 32

INDEX